ENTERTAINMENT TEC

CW00566401

In taking advantage of the latest in 'print on demand' digital printing techniques, Entertainment Technology Press is approaching book publishing in a very different way. By establishing a wide range of highly specific technical books that can be kept up-to-date in a continuing publishing process, our plan is to cover the entertainment technology sector with a wide range of individual titles.

As will be seen by examining the back cover of this book, the ETP list is divided into various categories so as to allow sufficient room for generic growth and development of each title. To ensure the quality of the books and the success of the project the publishers are building up a team of authors who are practising in and well-respected by the industry. As specialists within a particular field of activity it is anticipated that each author will stay closely involved with 'their' title or titles for an extended period.

All Entertainment Technology Press titles have a dedicated area on the publisher's own website at www.etnow.com where latest information and up-dates can be accessed by purchasers of the books concerned. This additional service is included within the purchase price of all titles.

Readers and prospective authors are invited to submit any ideas and comments they may have on the Entertainment Technology Press series to the Series Editor by email to editor@etnow.com.

Entertainment Technology Press Ltd
The Studio, High Green, Great Shelford, Cambridge CB2 5EG
Tel: +44 (0)1223 550805 Fax: +44 (0)1223 550806

AUTOCAD – A HANDBOOK FOR THEATRE USERS

David Ripley

ENTERTAINMENT TECHNOLOGY PRESS

Application & Techniques Series

To my long suffering wife and three daughters

AUTOCAD – A HANDBOOK FOR THEATRE USERS

David Ripley

Entertainment Technology Press

AutoCAD – A Handbook for Theatre Users

© David Ripley

First edition Published December 2004 by
Entertainment Technology Press Ltd
The Studio, High Green, Great Shelford, Cambridge CB2 5EG
Internet: www.etnow.com

ISBN 1 904031 31 5

A title within the
Entertainment Technology Press Aplication & Techniques Series
Series editor: John Offord

CODE / ACAD001

CONTENTS

—

ACKNOWLEDGEMENTS

Jerry Godden, for not giving me a job and making me learn about CAD.

Kevin Harland, CAD Tutor, Basingstoke College of Technology.

Tim Wills, Haymarket Theatre, Basingstoke, for paying!

Steve Green, Scottish Opera.

Sandy Maxwell, formerly of S4T.

All in the Department of Technical and Production Arts, RSAMD.

Geoff Joyce, ABTT.

Alistair Noonan and all at Central School of Speech and Drama.

Craig Hamilton at TMS In Education.

Finally, everyone who has taken up the AutoCAD for Theatre Course through S4T and the ABTT.

INTRODUCTION

AutoCAD® by Autodesk® is the most widely used CAD system in use today with over five million copies sold around the world. AutoCAD has been around for over 20 years and also provides the core technology for many other Autodesk products.

AutoCAD comes in two types: what might be described as 'full' AutoCAD and AutoCAD LT®. The main difference between the two is in the area of 3D functionality and cost.

AutoCAD is capable of taking a design from the initial 2D drawings through to a fully photorealistic 3D model using solids and surfaces and applying materials for rendering, whereas AutoCAD LT can create simple 3D drawings using lines and read 3D drawings up to a certain level only. It cannot for instance see the rendering on a completed model, but it can see shading but in a less sophisticated version than available in the full version. As a result, some parts of the book refer only to the full version, and where possible I have tried to indicate this.

This book covers AutoCAD 2000-2004 and is intended to guide a theatre user through the skills required to create a groundplan of a fictional theatre and also extend that drawing into the third dimension, add materials and finally render it. The book has been mainly written using AutoCAD 2004 so where any routines are not available to earlier releases I have indicated this. Please let me know if there are any that I have missed!

AutoCAD 2004 introduced a new version of the .dwg file format which is not compatible with earlier releases and for this reason the sample drawings required for the book are all saved in AutoCAD 2000's version of .dwg. These files can be obtained from www.etbooks.co.uk.

Defining CAD

There is often confusion as to what a CAD system is, what it does and what other, possibly similar systems can achieve.

When computerised drawing first started, it was initially referred to as CADD – Computer Aided Drawing and Design. These systems were initially very expensive and needed what were considered at the time high-powered machines, often mainframes, to run them. These machines could be quite specialised due to the way most CAD systems work.

As PCs became more sophisticated and relatively cheaper, the Maths co-processor required to run a CAD program became a standard part of the PC's architecture. When we moved into the era of 'Multimedia' PCs in the mid 1990s the Design and Drawing sides of CAD began to diverge, and can be broadly defined nowadays as follows.

CAD
Standing for **C**omputer **A**ided **D**raughting or **D**rawing

The first thing to note is the word *Aided,* this means the system helps you, but won't do it for you. It can automate various routine jobs, improve accuracy, show only what you want and make drawings clearer, but as with traditional Technical Drawing these are only techniques to apply in drawing your object.

The second word to note is *Draughting;* this system will not design for you; this process happens in your head, but will transfer those thoughts into a coherent shape on your monitor and ultimately onto paper.

Most CAD systems are used to produce 2 Dimensional, technical drawings. Although they can be capable of 3D drawing, other programs may cover this facet of the process better.

Computer Visualisation
Computer Visualisation deals in the 3 Dimensional aspects of design. It can encompass set design as well as lighting, costume and anything else required for a designer to communicate their intentions for a production.

Using a technique called rendering, the actual materials or paint finishes required can be accurately shown on screen, providing a Photo Realistic view of the production. Additionally, storyboards can be created providing a scene-by-scene narration as well as 'walk throughs' or 'fly bys'. Computer visualisation systems such as 3DS Max® by Discreet® are also available to both PC and Mac users.

CAD systems when used in tandem with a Computer Visualisation program produce the facts, figures and drawings that allow technical staff to reproduce the designer's intentions.

These definitions are not final; many people use a CAD systems 3D function for design and visualisation, whilst a lighting package such as WYSIWYG® has aspects of both.

For our purposes then we are dealing with a CAD system – AutoCAD. CAD systems can speed up your work, produce information and the drawings can be sent via email. They can be linked up so that differing departments' drawings cross-reference each other, ensuring that a master drawing is always up to date.

Whatever we call these programs or however we use them, our ultimate aim as it has always been is communication of ideas, thoughts and intentions in such a way that what was envisioned actually becomes a reality.

In many ways, what CAD programs produce is also one of the major pitfalls of them. This is largely due to people's perception of such systems as much as the systems themselves. A CAD drawing is apparently flawless, the lines are clear, symbols precise and the text always the same and legible. The same is not always true of a hand drawing. Because of this aesthetic and the knowledge that CAD drawings can be accurate to several decimal places the assumption is made that the CAD version is the more accurate.

CAD is just a tool the same way as a drawing board and a pencil are; the same errors that can be made on paper can be made on a PC. With the added complication of drawing in CAD at real-size then plotting to scale, rather than just drawing to scale throughout the process there is plenty of room for error. CAD Drawings therefore should be treated the same way as any other drawing, even though they may look more precise. RIRO – Rubbish In = Rubbish Out still applies, whichever method is used.

It should also be pointed out that you will get the best out of any CAD program if you have a basic understanding of technical drawing. Although many of AutoCAD's tools simplify drawing construction, the basic underpinning is still required to ensure accuracy.

Finally, with the best will in the world, an intuitive CAD system has yet to be produced. This is the Holy Grail of the design world, a program that as soon as you open it up allows you to naturally start drawing what you want easily and precisely. Although arguments rage about systems that are more intuitive than others according to their manufacturers and users, the truth is that most

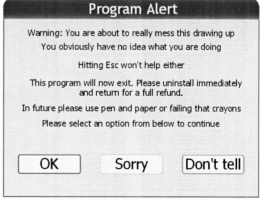

i-1 A typical Alert Dialogue from a truly intuitive CAD system.

of them open up with a bewildering array of menus, icons, dialogue boxes and palettes.

AutoCAD is no exception – hence this book – and although error messages can be quite baffling I haven't seen this one…yet! *Fig i-1.*

System Requirements

Here are the system requirements for AutoCAD 2004. As you can see, they are quite modest, although if you are doing a lot of rendering then a considerably larger amount of fast RAM is recommended. In this case, it is also worth considering using dual processors or having separate machines dedicated to rendering, known as a render farm.

Operating System	Windows 2000, XP Pro or Home
	Windows NT4 with SP6a or later
Processor	Pentium III 800mhz or equivalent
RAM	128Mb minimum
Display	1024 x 768 True Color
Hard Disk	300Mb for installation

Please note AutoCAD is not available for Mac OS. It will run via any Windows Emulator but at a reduced speed.

An AutoCAD Case Study – Small Change

The Haymarket Theatre in Basingstoke is a medium-size (400 seat) proscenium arch theatre set in a nineteenth century corn exchange *Fig i-2.* In 1999 the then artistic director decided to stage Peter Gill's *Small Change* set in Cardiff with a cast of four.

As this was a small-scale piece and the studio theatre at the local college we normally used was not thought suitable it was decided we would convert the Haymarket into an in-the-round studio space. Seats were to be put onstage and the stage area extended out beyond the orchestra pit apron. The actual set, designed by Elroy Ashmore, consisted of a square of playground ash, with a large old-fashioned roundabout, which was practical, in the centre and a high stool for each character in the corners of the square.

AutoCAD was used to plan the underlying structure of the stage extension as well as the onstage seating, in terms of risers and the number of seats that could be accommodated *Fig i-3.* This helped greatly in planning the budget expenditure and scheduling process.

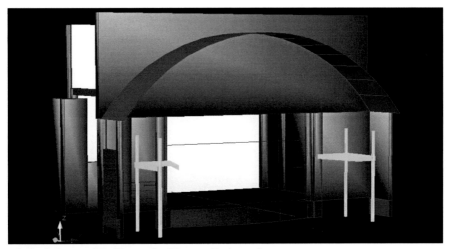

i-2 Shaded view of the Haymarket Theatre, Basingstoke.

However, the most important aspect of the process was to do with the licensing of the altered venue by the local authorities. By providing 3D rendered drawings to them, we were able to explain the arrangements for the audience access onto the stage seating as well as emergency exits directly off the stage *Fig i-4*. Amendments required by the Council or Fire Brigade could be easily added to the drawings and once the fit-up was complete, the licensing officers

*i-3 Shaded view of the Haymarket with seating, stage extension and **Small Change** set.*

i-4 Rendered view from the circle. Materials have been added and the model lit using AutoCAD lights to simulate lanterns.

were able to compare the renders with the actual show and grant the licence.

The one thing we didn't anticipate fully was the different acoustic upstage under the fly tower and downstage under the auditorium's barrel-vaulted ceiling, but with ingenious use of black wool serge masking this was also overcome.

By using the full functionality of AutoCAD, time, money and hassle were

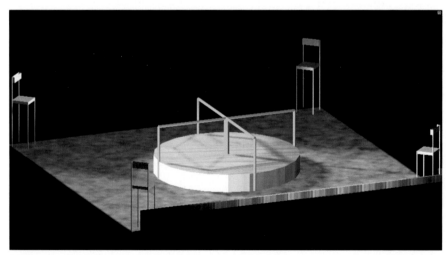

i-5 Rendered view from the back of the onstage seating bank.

reduced although this must obviously be weighed against the greater time producing drawings. However, overall, by using CAD in this situation, many of the potential problems could be solved well in advance and the council's visit to approve the venue was of the rubber-stamping variety due to our ability to show them what the stage would actually look like prior to the fit-up *Fig i-5, i-6.*

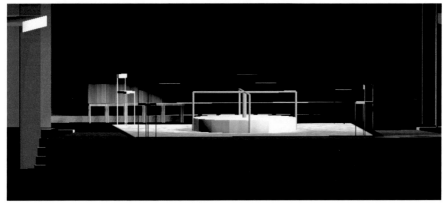

i-6 Rendered view from the normal stalls seats.

Although this exercise shows the power of AutoCAD in helping to solve complex design issues, it should always be remembered that it is still just a program that responds to inputs from a real person.

Using a program such as AutoCAD does not and should not replace basic design and technical drawing skills. Above all to create the models shown time was required for the Production team to get together and work the problem through.

Ultimately no piece of software can replace the creative team getting together and talking to each other. People are required to make those intuitive leaps so often required in a theatre. A grey box generating a stream of noughts and ones cannot make these links and hopefully will never replace the human element in a production's creative process.

1 SETTING UP

Before actually drawing anything, let's have a look around AutoCAD and its interface.

Click the Icon for your version of AutoCAD and wait for it to start up. If you don't have a desktop icon, it usually installs itself to Start \ Programs\Autodesk\AutoCAD.

The program will briefly show a splash screen detailing your name, AutoCAD serial number and supplier, and the program itself will appear. This may take a minute or so; be patient!

Depending on your version of AutoCAD you may see a Start up screen. You can generally just click OK to get into the program. See tip at end of chapter for details.

When AutoCAD has fully loaded, it should look like the screenshot *Fig 1-1*.

AutoCAD 2000(i)

AutoCAD 2002

AutoCAD 2004

AutoCAD LT2000

AutoCAD LT 2004

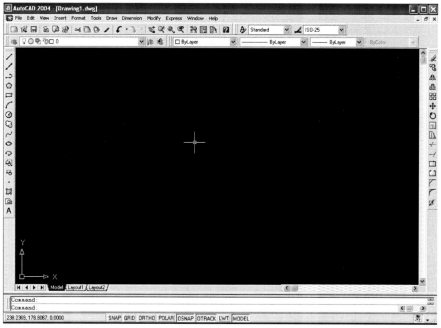

Fig 1-1 The basic AutoCAD program screen (AutoCAD 2004 shown).

Starting at the top of the Screen is the blue bar (called the Title Bar) showing the program and file name. In this case, the file is *(Drawing1.dwg)* which is the default title for a new drawing. To the right are the usual Minimise (_) Maximise (□) and Close (**X**) icons.

The next row down contains a series of drop down menus. Explore each one to see what's in them – not that it will make much sense at this stage! If you try something and get stuck, pressing ESC should clear things up. To the right again are the Min, Max and Close buttons. These refer to the current open drawing only and not the whole program.

Below this are two horizontal toolbars. The top left hand group are standard Windows icons. All the others are specialised AutoCAD functions. By placing your cursor over any of them a *tooltip* should appear, giving the name of the Icon. More information also appears in the bottom left corner of AutoCAD in an area shared with co-ordinate information. The second Toolbar is Object Properties, which deals with Layers and their appearance.

In the middle of the screen is a large black, blank area called the Drawing Area. In the bottom left hand corner of the Drawing Area is the UCS icon. This is a reference point you will need later to ensure drawing accuracy.

As you move your cursor into the Drawing Area, you will notice it changes from a normal Windows arrow to a cross with a square where the lines intersect. These are the Crosshairs. Where the two lines intersect is where you are pointing and drawing.

The Crosshairs are always shown in the plane which you are currently drawing in. As a result, they are not always as you see them now. The size of the Crosshairs can also be altered. I have mine set so that so that the lines always extend to the edge of the Drawing Area.

If you are running AutoCAD 2004 you may also find a Tool Palette floating in your AutoCAD Drawing Area when you first start up. This is a customisable method of inserting various frequently used items into a drawing. For now, switch it off by clicking on the **X** on the top of the Tool Palette's vertical blue bar.

To the left and right of the Drawing Area are two more toolbars.

*Fig 1-2
Draw
toolbar.*

These are the standard toolbars on start up: Draw *Fig 1-2* and Modify *Fig 1-3*, but you can have as many or as few as you need, docked or floating on the screen. To see other Toolbars, right click on any blank area in a toolbar and a list will come up. To move a toolbar, click on an area of the toolbar with no buttons and then drag it to where you wish to place it.

I have both Draw and Modify toolbars together on the right hand side of my screen. This is mainly because I am right handed so it is less distance to move my mouse.

At the bottom of the screen, below the Drawing Area, is a series of Excel style tabs: the one marked Model should be active. The other two are to do with Plotting and we will discuss these later.

Next down are two white strips, each with the word Command: on it. This is the Command or Prompt Line. The top one is the last command carried out: the one below is current. Here you input commands to AutoCAD. The commands also appear if you started doing something using the Menus or Toolbars.

Finally, at the bottom is the Status Bar – a line containing, from left to right, the co-ordinates of the cursor in relation to the UCS or Icon information and a series of buttons. To the far right is the Communication Center icon for updating AutoCAD. Other icons may also appear here according to what you are doing at the time.

You will now have found the three ways to get AutoCAD to do something: via the drop down Menus, the Toolbars and the Command Line. Any of these methods is valid and can be used together. It may be easier to type a command than continually moving the mouse. You will gradually find your own way of working, which will combine the various methods.

Move the Crosshairs around the screen and notice the co-ordinates change in the bottom left hand of the screen. Now click on the SNAP button on the Status Bar at the bottom of the screen. Notice how the cursor is now jumping rather than moving smoothly.

Next click GRID. A grid of dots will appear and when you move the cursor, it jumps from point to point. These two tools can be useful in drawing accurately. Switch them both off for now. They can also be toggled on or off using F9 for Snap and F7 for Grid.

You may have noticed that the grid did not fill the entire screen. It

Fig 1-3
Modify
toolbar.

only fills the area defined by the Drawing Limits. AutoCAD has a sheet of A3 at 1:1 as its default drawing screen, which is 420mm wide by 297mm deep. Width (left to right) is referred to as the X-axis and is always first in co ordinates, whilst Depth (top to bottom) is Y. A positive number is either up or to the right of the UCS, a negative figure below or to the left. To help you further, the UCS Icon is marked with the axes.

Limits

The rule of CAD is: *Always draw your objects full size.*

AutoCAD tells you in its literature that you can draw in any units, Miles, Centimetres, Yards, Cubits, Parsecs – whatever you choose. This is very nice until it comes to plotting (printing) your drawing to scale. It is at this point you choose your units, either inches or millimetres. It is better to start working in one unit and stick with it throughout all your drawings. In our case it is generally the metric measuring system, so our unit of choice is millimetres (mm).

On paper, if I want to draw a line 1000mm or 1m long and I draw it at 1:25, I will draw a line 4cm long. In AutoCAD, I draw a line 1000mm long and it is actually 1000mm long. It is only when printed it is scaled.

An A0 sheet is 1189mm x 841mm. In order to set our screen to this size but ready to plot at 1:25 it is therefore logical to multiply our sheet size by 25.

This gives us a sheet size of 29725mm x 21025mm.

At the Command Line Type `Limits` You do not have to click in the Command Line to enter commands, just start typing and it will appear.

```
Specify lower left corner or [ON/OFF]
<0.0000,0.0000>: Press ↵

Specify upper right corner
<420.0000,297.0000>:   Enter 29725,21025 ↵
```

Next Type Z ↵ A. This zooms the screen out so that your new limits fit to the edge of the screen. Move your mouse around to see the difference in the co-ordinate area.

Now that we have a Drawing area big enough to work with, let's look at some of the Drawing Aids AutoCAD gives us.

Drafting Settings

Now we know the area of our drawing, we can make sensible decisions about SNAP and GRID settings.

Click on Tools ➤ Drafting Settings *Fig 1-4.*

In both Snap and Grid areas select On to turn them on. Next in Grid X set a distance of 1000. Hitting Tab will copy this to the Y value. This will set the dots of the grid at a spacing of 1 metre across the drawing area.

It may be useful to set the Snap to a distance less than the Grid, typically half the former's value.

Type 500 in Snap X and Tab, again this copies the value to the Y value. Click on OK to exit this box.

Fig 1-4 Drafting settings dialogue box.

Switch on both Grid and Snap and observe the results on screen. These may not be ideal settings; they are only an example. Be aware of too small a gap between dots on the Grid. AutoCAD will not display too dense a Grid and will tell you so. You will probably not need Snap and Grid to always be active.

There are a couple of other Drawing Aids but we will look at those in the next Chapter when we will need them whilst creating our theatre groundplan.

Precision (Drawing Units)

Let us now set our decimal place for the precision of units. As we are dealing with millimetres an accuracy of .0 will suffice. The default is .0000, which is a bit excessive.

Click Format ➤ Units and the Drawing Units dialog box appears, *Fig 1-5.*

The radio button is already selecting decimal. Click on the drop down box marked Precision and change it to 0.0. Click OK

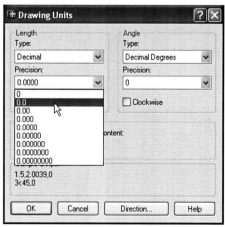

Fig 1-5 Drawing units dialogue box.

Options

The Options dialogue box has several tabs to alter various parameters of AutoCAD. Clicking on the tabs gives access to these settings, which are editable. Not all of these are worth changing as the defaults, in many cases, work fine.

Click Tools ➢ Options and the Options dialog box will be displayed. We will now work through the useful tabs.

Profiles

Although this is set to the furthest right we will look at this tab first, as if you wish to save any changes as you go, you need to have created a profile to save them to. *Fig 1-6.*

The profile named <<Unnamed Profile>> is the default and is the screen format you see the first time you open AutoCAD.

To create your Profile, Click on Add to List button and wait for the dialog box to appear. *Fig 1-7*

Call your profile anything you like; you can add a description if you wish. Click Apply & Close, which returns you to the previous window.

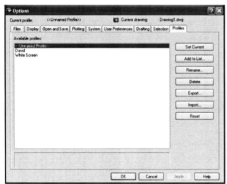

Fig 1-6 Options – Profiles tab.

Fig 1-7 Add profile box.

Your Profile name should be in the box now with a description in the grey box at the bottom. Highlight it and Click Set Current. This Profile is now active and any changes you make and apply will become part of this profile.

The Rename button enables you to change the details in the Name window of a profile, either the actual name or details of the description.

Delete is obvious. Export allows you to save a profile to disc, whilst Import allows you to load a previously saved Profile. This is useful if you go offsite and use another machine. Using Import, it is easy to set the PC up to your preferences.

Reset will reset a profile back to the standard defaults.

Having now created our Profile we can move on to the other tabs we want to amend. Unfortunately Profiles are not included in the Options dialog box of AutoCAD LT so you will need to manually reset any changes made, if required.

Display

This tab controls the appearance of AutoCAD. The top left box is titled Window Elements *Fig 1-8*.

The first tick box is *Display scroll bars in drawing window*. These again reduce the drawing area size, so I do not recommend them. There are plenty of ways within AutoCAD to move around your drawing and these work the same as the Pan command. They are on by default.

The bottom boxes are titled *Colors* and *Fonts* and allow you to set the way AutoCAD presents itself onscreen. Click on to *Colors* and the Color Options dialog box is presented. *Fig 1-9*

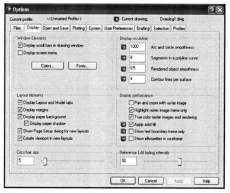

Fig 1-8 Options – Display dialogue.

You can change the colours on the different parts of the screen according to taste. Black is the default for the drawing screen. I prefer blue with white text for the Command Line but you can choose any combination you fancy.

To change the colour either pick an area on the schematic at the top left or select from the drop down box marked *Window Element*. Then choose your colour from the standard palette offered or one of AutoCAD special colours via Select color – at the bottom of the drop down menu. When you have made your selection Click Apply & Close to return to the previous dialog box.

Fonts offer you the choice of any fonts installed on your computer, together with style and size. *Fig 1-10*

Remember, when altering the font, colours

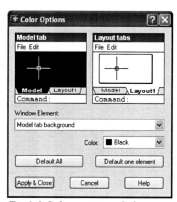

Fig 1-9 Colour options dialogue.

Fig 1-10 Command Line window font dialogue.

etc, you will still need to be able to see what appears on the screen, so keep it simple and not too garish!

Click OK to return to the Display dialog box and then Click Apply & Close. The changes will now take effect.

Below that is the Crosshair size selection box. Here you set the lengths of the crosshairs. 100% means they always touch the side, which I personally find useful as a reference, but it can be set to any size by moving the slider. The default is 5%.

Nothing else on this tab is worth tampering with now so now click on the Open & Save tab.

Open & Save

There are two elements to look at here *Fig 1-11*.

The first is the *File Save - Save As* area. As you can see, I make my default to save .dwg files as AutoCAD 2000 format.

There are reasons for this. AutoCAD 2004's .dwg format is new and cannot be read by the older versions of AutoCAD. If you are exchanging data with users of most other CAD programs, they also cannot yet read the 2004 .dwg format. It is therefore easier to save as an AutoCAD 2000 file to ensure compatibility.

Below that is a box titled *File Safety Precautions*. AutoCAD's default automatic save time is a potentially disastrous 120 minutes (2 hours). There is nothing more frustrating than a problem with your PC 1 hour 59 minutes into a drawing, which means you lose all that work. Change the box to 10 and click Apply.

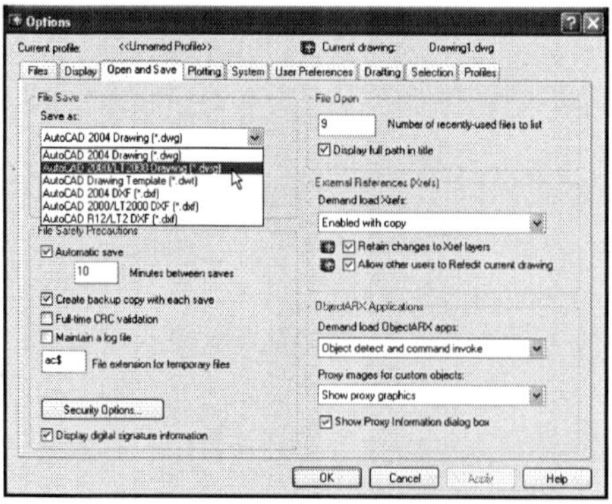

Temporary save files are saved as .ac$, whilst back-up files are saved with the extension .bak. To restore them if you have had a crash, find the file, change the extension to .dwg and then open the file. This requires a bit of fiddling in Windows Explorer or My Computer to show the extensions of files.

Fig 1-11 Options – Open & Save tab.

User Preferences

Fig 1-12: We can start at the top left box, *Windows Standard Behavior.* Both Windows Standard Accelerator Keys and Shortcut Menus in drawing area are the default. I personally find the menus slow me down but they do have their use. You can have the best of both worlds by clicking on *Right Button Customization Fig 1-13.*

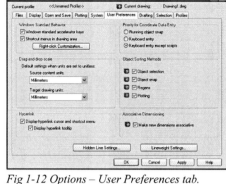

Fig 1-12 Options – User Preferences tab.

Check the *Turn on time-sensitive right-click* box. Make the Longer click duration 250 milliseconds as shown. Click Apply & Close. Now when you right click at the end of a command, a normal click will repeat the command, whilst holding the button will allow the sub menu to pop up. Unfortunately this option only came in with AutoCAD 2004. Prior to this you can define only what happens when you right click. The default is that a sub menu will appear but you can change it to just repeating the last command, for instance.

Next down is the area that deals with units within the AutoCAD DesignCenter. Using the drop downs, change it to the units you usually work in. millimetres is the recommended drawing unit in the UK.

The rest of the defaults on this tab are generally the best options, so once again click Apply to save your changes. Then click OK to leave the Options dialogue box.

We will need this drawing, or rather blank sheet later. The best thing therefore is to turn it into a Drawing Template or .dwt file. This will save you having to remember to save it with a new name if you save it as a .dwg file now. This is simple to do.

Click File ➢ Save as. When the dialog

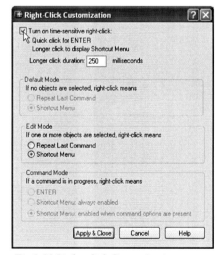

Fig 1-13 Right-click Customisation dialogue.

box appears pick AutoCAD Drawing Template (.dwt) from the drop down box at the bottom. *Fig 1-14*.

The location where your file is to be saved will change to the Templates folder. Name your file A0@1-25 will do and click Save.

This template is now accessible via File ➤ New.

Fig 1-14 Save Drawing As dialogue.

Exercise 1

As we are drawing objects of varying sizes, you should now set up some different sheets to use.

Try creating the following:
A1, A2, A3 and A4 @ 1:25
A0, A1, A2, A3 and A4 @ 1:50
A4 @ 1:1

Save them all as Templates; they may be useful later.

Remember we ideally want the drawing we are creating to be easy to see as we draw it.

Think about the size of some of the objects you will be asked to draw and use a suitable sheet size.

ISO Metric paper sizes   *1:50*

A0	841mm x 1187mm
A1	594mm x 841mm
A2	420mm x 594mm
A3	297mm x 420mm *14850 x 21000*
A4	210mm x 297mm
A5	148mm x 210mm

Chapter Tips

Tip!

Depending on the version of AutoCAD you are running there are a range of options as to what happens when you first start the program.

Firstly you may see nothing and AutoCAD will just start up as shown at the start of the chapter.

Alternatively, if you are running either AutoCAD 2000 or 2004 you may see what is described as the (traditional) startup dialogue box. *Fig B1-1.*

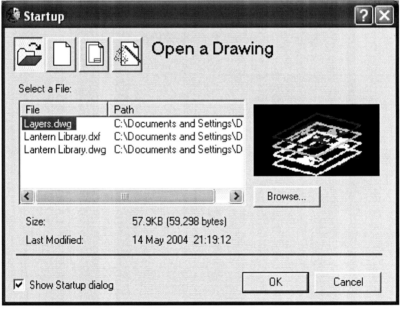

Fig B1-1 Startup dialogue box (AutoCAD 2000 LT) Note the Show Startup dialogue option check box.

The icons at the top from left to right are: Open a Drawing; Start from Scratch; Use a Template; Use a Wizard.

Finally, if you are using either AutoCAD 2000i or 2002 you will see AutoCAD Today, a short lived idea offering access to the same options as above in a more sophisticated way *Fig B1-2*. Using Internet connectivity Today also checks for updates via the Autodesk Point A portal and allows you to set up a notice board for other users.

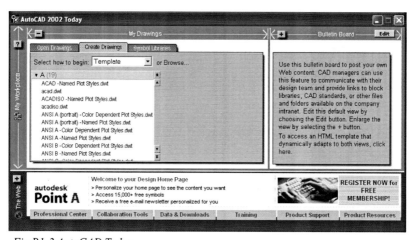

Fig B1-2 AutoCAD Today.

All of these choices are accessed via the Options Dialog Box — System Tab *Fig B1-3.* Under *General Options* is a drop down box marked *Startup:* depending on your version of AutoCAD the options above can be selected here.

In some versions of AutoCAD LT the option not to show a startup dialog box is a check box on the dialog box as in Fig B1-1

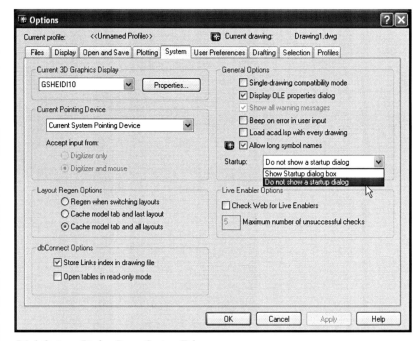

B1-3 Options Dialog Box – System Tab.

Draw and Modify Toolbar Details

Draw Toolbar

Modify Toolbar

Line

Construction Line

Polyline

Polygon

Rectangle

Arc

Circle

Revision Cloud

Spline

Ellipse

Ellipse Arc

Insert Block

Make Block

Point

Hatch

Region

Multiline Text

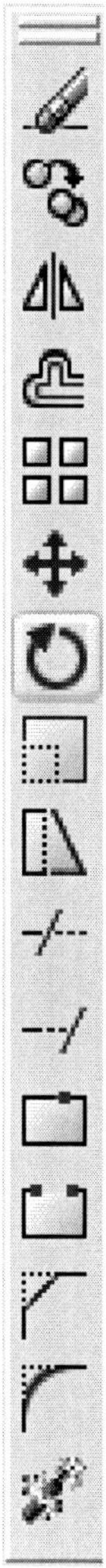

Erase

Copy

Mirror

Offset

Array

Move

Rotate

Scale

Stretch

Trim

Extend

Break at Point

Break

Chamfer

Fillet

Explode

2 STARTING TO DRAW

Open a new drawing, using one of your templates. For the first part of this Chapter, size really doesn't matter.

Defining points on our drawing area creates lines. Each point has a coordinate, which can be created either with a mouse click or by typing in figures in various formats explained below. Lines have no thickness in themselves but so that we can see them, AutoCAD's are 1 pixel wide.

To draw a line either:

> Click Draw ➢ Line
> or Click the Line Icon on the Draw Toolbar
> or Type Line or L ↵ at the Command Line.

In any case, the following will appear at the command line:

Line icon

    _line Specify first point:

For now, just click anywhere on the Drawing Area. Move the cursor away from the point and notice that a line from your first point is also stuck to the crosshairs of the cursor. This is called Rubberbanding; you will see it often in a variety of guises. Move the cursor around and wherever you wish; Left click and then carry on, repeating the left clicks. Create a shape of your choice, such as *Fig 2-1*.

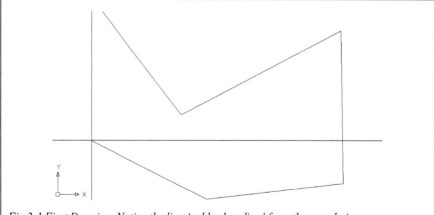
Fig 2-1 First Drawing. Notice the line 'rubberbanding' from the crosshairs.

When you have enough lines either press ↵ or Right Click. If a sub menu appears onscreen, click on Enter and the command is completed.

Moving Around the Drawing Area

You will need on occasion to work on a certain part of a drawing. To do this you will need to use Zoom and Pan commands. A simple way of using them is via the middle wheel on your mouse.

Scrolling the wheel towards the screen will zoom in: scrolling away zooms out. The zoom is centred on the middle of the screen, which may not be what you want to look at. To move the view from side to side or up and down, hold the wheel down. The Pan cursor will appear. Keep the button held down and move the mouse.

Zoom has some other useful options; Type Z ↵ and look at the command line:

```
Specify corner of window, enter a scale
factor (nX or nXP), or
[All/Center/Dynamic/Extents/Previous/Scale/
Window] <real time>:
```

Here are the ones you are likely to use most often:

All	Zooms out to the Limits of the Drawing. We have already used this on setting our Limits
Extents	Zooms out to the edges of the objects you have drawn
Previous	Returns you to the last Zoom action
Window	Create a window around the area you want to zoom into.

You can do this directly without typing W. Left Click in the drawing area and then drag out a window keeping the button held down. Release when the area is enclosed and left click again, the drawing will zoom in.

To select any of the alternatives, type in the initial letter of the command at the command line and ↵

Erasing Objects

Now we have some scribble on the screen, let's get rid of it.
Either Click Edit ➤ Clear
or Click the Erase Icon on the Modify Toolbar
or Type Erase or E ↵ at the Command line.
The prompt displays

Erase
icon

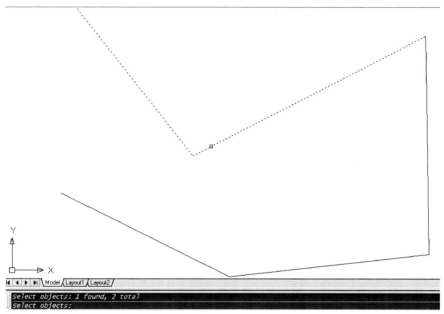

Fig 2-2 Object selection using the Pick Box.

```
Select objects:
```
Notice the crosshairs have changed to a box called the Pick Box. Now Left click on some of the lines, they will change to dashed lines. The Command Line will count the number of objects you have picked, including any duplicates. *See Fig 2-2.*

When you have picked a few, right click and they will disappear. Now enter U ↵ (for Undo) at the Command Line and the lines reappear.

Reissue the Erase command a different way from last time. This time, when the Pick Box appears, move it to the top right hand side of the screen and Left click and hold the button down. Now move the mouse towards the bottom left hand side of the screen; a dashed box attached to your first point will follow you. Left click again, then either right click or ↵ and those lines which touched the box will disappear. This is known as a Crossing Window and is often used when selecting objects. *See Fig 2-3 overleaf.*

Undo again, this time using the Undo Icon on the Standard Toolbar. Select Erase again and create another window, but this time from Left to Right. This box is solid and when you right click only lines

Undo icon

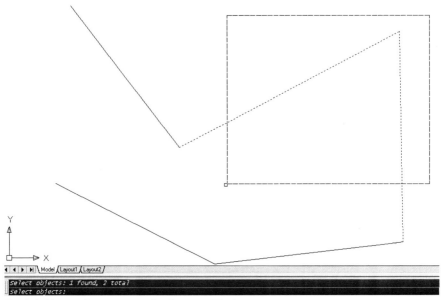

Fig 2-3 Object selection using the Crossing Window.

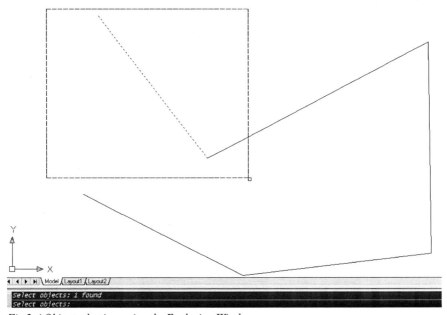

Fig 2-4 Object selection using the Enclosing Window.

completely within the Window are erased, as shown in *Fig 2-4*. *This is known as an Enclosing Window.*

Lastly, issue the erase command again and at the Command Line Type `all` ↵. The number of object selected will be shown. Press Enter. Everything left should now be erased.

Drawing Accurately

The advantage of AutoCAD and similar systems is that they allow you to draw extremely accurately. This is done in a variety of ways using the coordinate system. Let us examine them.

Firstly, using what you have learnt so far, try to draw a square, each side being equal. You will probably end up with something less than square (unless you used SNAP and GRID) and you will have no control over its size. What is required is a system for specifying sizes and distances. There are in fact several.

Before starting the next section open an appropriate sheet size. The objects we will be drawing require an area of about 2500 x 2500.

Absolute Coordinates

Imagine using the A-Z to find a street. Firstly you look along the top for a number then go down the number of squares to find the point. These are Absolute coordinates, also known as Cartesian coordinates.

Three axes signify the coordinate system. They are:

X, which runs from left to right horizontally across the screen

Y, which runs from bottom to top vertically across the screen

Z, which runs out of the screen towards you and is used extensively in 3D drawing.

AutoCAD sets the Origin, 0,0,0 at the bottom left corner of the screen.

As a result of this any lines moving to the right or up are

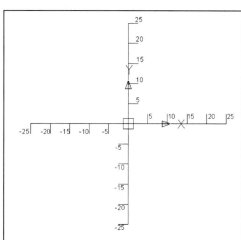

Fig 2-5 Cartesian Coordinates. The UCS is at the World Coordinate System, origin 0,0,0,.

positive figures, whilst anything to the left or down is negative. This is shown in *Fig 2.5*

Let's draw a shape with the bottom left corner 100 in and 100 up from 0,0 where the UCS is.

Issue the Line command however you feel easiest with.

When the prompt reads:

```
_line Specify first point
```
Enter 100,100 ↵ (Note the comma)

The prompt reads:
```
Specify next point or [Undo]
```
Enter 1400,100 ↵

The prompt reads:
```
Specify next point or [Undo]
```
Enter 1400,2100 ↵

The prompt reads:
```
Specify next point or [Undo]
```
Enter 100,2100 ↵

The prompt reads:
```
Specify next point or [Undo]
```
Enter 100,100 ↵

Or C (Close)

You will have a nice rectangle (unless it's all gone horribly wrong) but you probably can't see much of it. Use your mouse wheel to zoom out until you can. Pan the drawing until it's centred up. *Fig 2-6.*

If the drawing isn't right, retrace your steps. By entering C or Close, the line will automatically find the start point of this continuous set of lines.

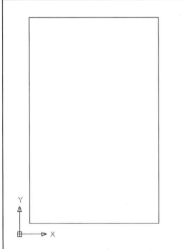

Fig 2-6 First rectangle created using Absolute Coordinates.

Relative Coordinates

These coordinates allow you to draw in reference to another position. It uses the

@ symbol before the distance you want the line to be drawn. So for instance, @50,100 means 50 to the right and 100 up from your starting point. You would end up with a left to right rising diagonal line.

Issue the Line command and specify the start point as 200,100

The prompt reads:

`Specify next point or [Undo]`
`Enter @0,1900 ↵`

The prompt reads:

`Specify next point or [Undo]`
`Enter @1100,0 ↵`

The prompt reads:

`Specify next point or [Undo]`
`Enter @0,-1900 ↵` Note the minus sign

The prompt reads:

`Specify next point or [Undo]`
`Enter @-1100,0 ↵` Again note the minus

Or *(Close)*

This should have created another rectangle, inside the first one. *Fig 2-7.*

Polar Coordinates

Polar Coordinates are similar to Relative except they use a distance from the start point, combined with an angle. For example @100<45 means 100 units away from the point at an angle of 45°.

AutoCAD treats angles as always having 0° to the East or right. So using the clock face:

  ⊕   3 o'clock = 0°
  ◷   12 o'clock = 90°
  ◶   9 o'clock = 180°
  ◴   6 o'clock = 270°

Always bear this in mind when using Polar Coordinates. Having a calculator handy is also useful!

Issue the Line command and specify the

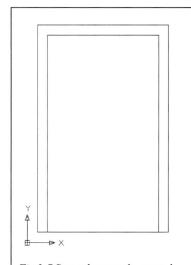

Fig 2-7 Second rectangle created using Relative Coordinates.

start point as 300,1900

The prompt reads:

```
Specify next point or [Undo]
```

Enter @900<270 ↵

The prompt reads:

```
Specify next point or [Undo]
```

Enter @400<0 ↵

The prompt reads:

```
Specify next point or [Undo]
```

Enter @900<90 ↵

The prompt reads:

```
Specify next point or [Undo]
```

Enter @400<180 ↵

Or C (Close)

This will create another rectangle within the second one but in its top left hand corner. *Fig 2-8*

You have now learnt how to draw a line and make a series of them into shapes. You can also get rid of them.

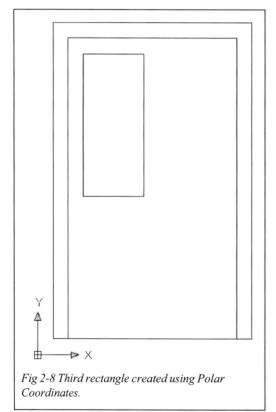

Fig 2-8 Third rectangle created using Polar Coordinates.

Exercise 2

Complete the drawing by adding the rectangles
shown in *Fig 2 Ex1* (It's a four-panel door). Do not
add the dimensions!

Use all three methods: Absolute, Relative and Polar.

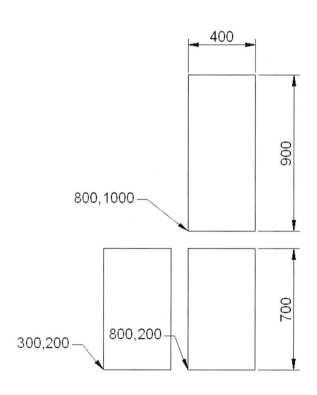

Fig 2 Ex 1 Completed drawing with dimension information.

Starting the Theatre Drawing

Open up your A0 1:25 Sheet.

Firstly we will use the Rectangle command to create a border. Borders are useful to define an area in which all information is enclosed. This also helps when you are checking plotted drawings again to make sure nothing has fallen off the edge of the paper when it was printed.

Start the Rectangle command:

Either Click Draw ➢ Rectangle

or Click the Rectangle Icon on the Draw Toolbar

or Type `rectang` at the Command line.

Specify first corner point or

Rect-angle icon.

```
Chamfer/Elevation/Fillet/Thickness/Width]:
100,100 ↵
```

Specify other corner point or

```
[Dimensions]: 29625,20925 ↵
```

In this case, we have used absolute coordinates to specify both corners of the Rectangle. The corners are the diagonally opposite ones and we can use any other method of defining them including just picking. Alternatively we could have specified the size by using the Dimension Option.

Specify your first point 100,100 then type d instead of giving the next corner. The command line changes as follows:

```
Specify length for rectangles <0>: 29625
```

Length is in the X axis

```
Specify width for rectangles <0>: 20925
```

Width is in the Y axis

```
Specify other corner point or [Dimensions]:
```

Click onscreen, depending on where you click, the rectangle will form. For example, if you pick in the positive XY plane (up and right of your start point) the rectangle is formed exactly as above. However if you click in the negative XY plane, that is below and left of where you started this rectangle, then that start point becomes the top right corner of the box.

Object Snap (OSNAP)

Next we will define our centre line using the Object Snaps. Object Snaps or OSNAPS allow you to pick accurate points on objects from which to draw.

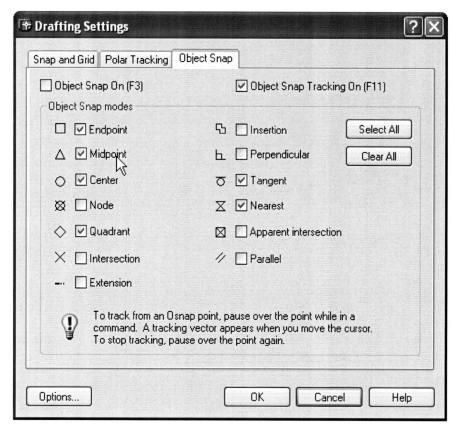

Fig 2-9 Drafting Settings dialog box – Object Snap options.

These include Endpoints of a line, the Center of a circle, etc. To access the OSNAP settings, Right Click the OSNAP button on the Status Bar then pick Settings from the menu that appears.

In the dialog box *Fig 2-9* make sure Midpoint is selected (its marker is a triangle) then click OK and make sure the OSNAP button is on (F3 has the same function).

We will now create our Centre Line

```
Command: _line Specify first point:
```
Pick the Midpoint of the top horizontal line ⏎

```
Specify next point or [Undo]:
```
Pick the Mid point of the bottom horizontal line ⏎

```
Specify next point or [Undo]: ↵
```
The next job is to start drawing our Proscenium Arch. Follow the instructions below.
```
Command: LINE
Specify first point: 20650,7600 ↵
Specify next point or [Undo]: @0,-200 ↵
Specify next point or [Undo]: ↵
```
Now zoom in to the bottom right hand corner of our sheet so you can see what you are doing.
```
Command: z
ZOOM
Specify corner of window, enter a scale
factor (nX or nXP), or
[All/Center/Dynamic/Extents/Previous/Scale/
Window] <real time>:
Specify opposite corner:
```
Drag a window out to the size you want and left click. The drawing will zoom in to the area you have defined.

Now start drawing again.
```
Command: _line Specify first point:
```
Pick the bottom of your first line using Endpoint.
```
Specify next point or [Undo]: @250<310 ↵
Specify next point or [Undo]: @250,0 ↵
Specify next point or [Close/Undo]: @0,-100 ↵
Specify next point or [Close/Undo]: @500,0 ↵
Specify next point or [Close/Undo]: @0,100 ↵
Specify next point or [Close/Undo]: @3000<0 ↵
Specify next point or [Undo]: @0,-3000 ↵
Specify next point or [Undo]: ↵
Specify next point or [Close/Undo]: ↵
```
Now draw the Stage Left Wall.
```
Command: _line Specify first point:
```

Pick the top of your first line using Endpoint.

```
Specify next
point or [Undo]:
@4000,0 ↵
Specify next
point or [Undo]:
@11300<90 ↵
Specify next
point or [Close/
Undo]: ↵
```

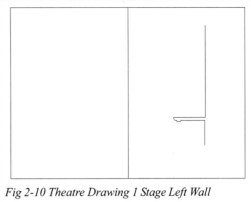

Fig 2-10 Theatre Drawing 1 Stage Left Wall

Fig 2-10 shows what you should now have drawn. Remember to use Undo if it goes wrong!

Ortho and Mirror

Let us for ease assume our theatre is symmetrical. Rather than draw a replica of our proscenium and wall we can use editing functions to save time.

Firstly we need to use Ortho to ensure we are restricted to right angles only. This is done by clicking the button on the Status bar or F8. By using this function we will make sure our Mirror is accurate.

Firstly though we need to be able to see the whole page.

```
Command: z
ZOOM
Specify corner of window, enter a scale
factor (nX or nXP), or
[All/Center/Dynamic/Extents/Previous/Scale/
Window] <real time>: e ↵
```

Next start Mirror
Either Click Modify ➢ Mirror
or Click the Mirror Icon on the Modify Toolbar
or Type Mirror ↵ at the Command line.

Mirror icon.

```
Command: _mirror
Select objects:
```

Use a crossing window to grab the lines you have just created:

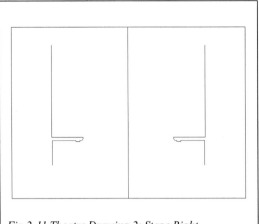

Fig 2-11 Theatre Drawing 2: Stage Right Wall added.

```
Specify opposite
corner: 10 found
```

```
Select objects: ↵
```

```
Specify first
point of mirror
line:
```

Select a point on the Centre Line. The Intersection OSNAP should appear. Pick it.

```
Specify second
point of mirror
line:
```

Keep on the Centre Line and pick again using the OSNAP to be sure.

```
Delete source objects? [Yes/No] <N>:↵
```

We should now have the drawing in *Fig 2-11*. To use Mirror you need an object to Mirror and a line to define the axis about which you Mirror. It is easiest to think of turning the page of this book. The front of the page is your object and the spine the axis about which you work.

Copy

As we have seen above when using AutoCAD, once an object is created it can be re-used. We will see more of this later, but this can be applied to all sorts of things. The rule therefore is:

Never draw the same thing twice.

We now need to put a back wall onto our theatre and we will use Copy to do this. First though we need to create our shape to copy. The back wall consists of pillars 500 wide by 200 deep set into the wall supporting the fly tower, with 2 metres of brickwork in between them.

Zoom into the top (upstage) end of the Stage Left wall and draw the following:

```
Command: _line Specify first point:
```

Pick the Endpoint of the SL wall.

```
Specify next point or [Undo]: @-500,0 ↵
Specify next point or [Undo]: @0,200 ↵
Specify next point or [Close/Undo]: @-2000,0 ↵
Specify next point or [Close/Undo]: ↵
```

We now need to add a return to the right hand end of the pillar section, so copy the existing return and place it as follows:

Either Click Modify ➢ Copy

or Click the Copy Icon on the Modify Toolbar

or Type Copy ↵ at the command line

```
    Command: _copy
```

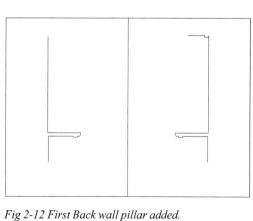

*Copy
icon*

Select objects:

Pick the 200 long vertical line

```
1 found
Select objects: ↵
Specify base point or displacement, or
[Multiple]:
```

   Pick the bottom endpoint of this vertical line ↵

```
Specify second point of displacement or <use
first point as displacement>:
```

Pick the Endpoint at the top of the SL Wall ↵

   Your drawing should now look like *Fig 2-12.*

   Now Zoom out so you can see both walls. We need to place five more of these wall sections across the back so start the Copy command again.

```
Select objects:
1 found
```

Use the pick box to select the right vertical ↵

```
Select objects:
```

Use a crossing window for the rest.

Fig 2-12 First Back wall pillar added.

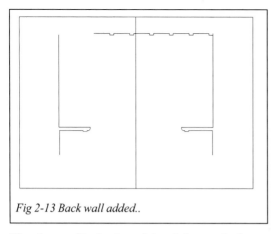

Fig 2-13 Back wall added..

```
Specify opposite
corner: 3 found,
4 total
Select objects:
↵
Specify base
point or
displacement, or
[Multiple]: m
```
Use Multiple to save time
```
Specify base
point:
```

Use the top Endpoint of the right vertical.

```
Specify second point of displacement or <use
first point as
displacement>:
```

Pick the left Endpoint of our wall section and repeat five times.

We now have most of a back wall. *Fig 2-13.* We want to place some dock doors in it Upstage Right so next we will use the OSNAP command to create a gap.

```
Command: _line Specify first point:
```

Pick the left Endpoint of the back wall

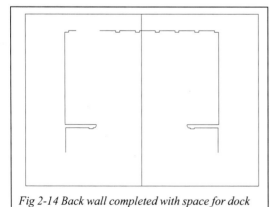

Fig 2-14 Back wall completed with space for dock doors.

```
Specify next
point or [Undo]:
```
Just hit ↵
```
Command:LINE
```
Restart the Line command:
```
Specify first
point: @-3000,0
```
This is a Relative Coordinate. We are starting our line −3000 from the endpoint of the back wall, thus creating our gap.

```
Specify next point or [Undo]: @-975,0
Specify next point or [Undo]:
```

To complete the back wall copy as much of the pillar section as you require to fill in the remaining space. Then go to the corner of USL and delete the vertical we created for our pillar. *Fig 2-14*

Offset

We have now created our basic theatre shape but as yet our walls have no thickness. The Offset command allows us to copy a line at a specific distance away quickly and easily.

Either Click Modify ➢ Offset

or Click the Offset Icon on the Modify Toolbar

or Type Offset ↵ at the command line

```
Command: _offset
Specify offset distance or [Through]
<Through>:
```

Offset icon.

Through allows you to set the distance using the mouse. We have a specific distance in mind :

```
500 ↵
Select object to offset or <exit>:
```

Work around the walls picking them and then clicking on their offstage side, until you have created the drawing in *Fig 2-15*

To complete the back wall, we need to fill in any of the gaps above the pillars and at the corners. Use Line and Copy for the pillars.

Extend

Using this command we can define a boundary then extend a line to meet it. The resultant line is one object.

We can also extend lines

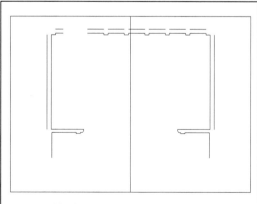

Fig 2-15 Thickness added to walls using Offset.

using an implied boundary. In this mode AutoCAD will calculate where two lines would meet if they were extended and then extend them to that point. This is ideal for our corners.

Either Click Modify ➢ Extend

or Click the Extend Icon on the Modify Toolbar

  or Type Extend ↵ at the command line:

Extend icon.

```
Command: _extend
Current settings: Projection=UCS,
Edge=None
Select boundary edges ...
Select objects:
```

Pick one of the two lines you have just created with Offset at the USL corner

```
1 found ↵
Select objects:
```

Pick the other line at the same corner:

```
1 found, 2 total
Select objects: ↵
Select object to extend or shift-select to
trim or [Project/Edge/Undo]:
e ↵
```

Enter an implied edge extension mode

```
[Extend/No extend] <No extend>: e ↵
```

This allows the implied edges to work

```
Select object to extend or shift-select to
trim or [Project/Edge/Undo]:
```

Pick either line and it will extend to where the other one would intersect it. You will need to pick the end of the line closest to where you want the lines to meet.

```
Select object to extend or shift-select to
trim or [Project/Edge/Undo]:
```

Pick the closest end of other line and it will meet the first

```
Select object to extend or shift-select to
trim or [Project/Edge/Undo]: ↵
```

When you are happy with that process repeat it for the other side.

Finally we will create the Safety Curtain for the theatre. Start the Rectangle command

```
Command: _rectang
Specify first corner point or [Chamfer/
Elevation/Fillet/Thickness/Width]:
8913,7603
Specify other corner point or [Dimensions]:
@12000,250
```

Check that it all looks like *Fig 2-16* and save the drawing!

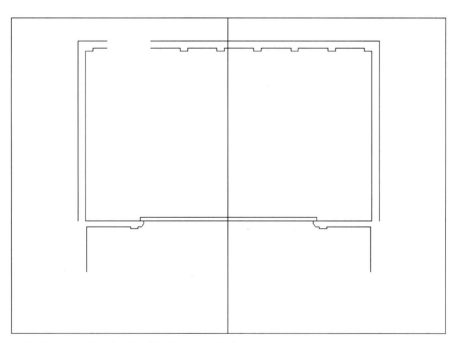

2-16 Walls completed and Safety Curtain added.

The UCS/WCS Icon

Tip!

The appearance of the UCS/WCS Icon varies not only according to the version of AutoCAD you are running but also the mode you are drawing in.

The UCS in AutoCAD 2000 is shown in *Fig B2-1*. This is actually a WCS, indicated by the W at the intersection of the axes.

From 2000i onwards, the standard UCS looks like *Fig B2 —2* with a box at the intersection now showing when it is at the Origin.

For 3D work up until 2000 the UCS remained the same but from 2000i onwards in 3D mode the Z axis is also shown. This helps greatly in orientating yourself to the current drawing plane. *Fig B2-3*

If you then use Shade on a 3D model the UCS changes again to become a coloured, 3D icon as shown in *Fig B2-4*

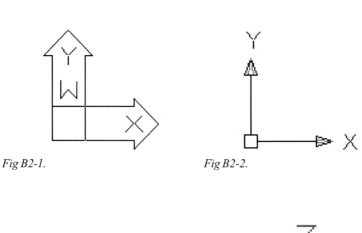

Fig B2-1.

Fig B2-2.

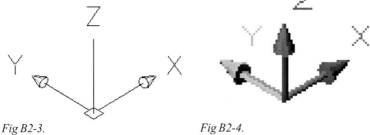

Fig B2-3.

Fig B2-4.

3 OBJECT PROPERTIES

Everything you draw in AutoCAD is an object. Every object in AutoCAD has several properties, many of which are editable.

In some ways, we have already changed some objects' properties when using an editing command such as Extend as we did in the last chapter. By using Extend we change the length of a line from one value to another.

One set of properties we need to use more frequently than others are Layers, Linetypes and Colours. These have their own toolbars, which are amongst the default ones shown at start up. As they are side by side they actually look like one and for all intents and purposes they are *Fig 3-1 Fig 3-2.*

Fig 3-1 The Layers toolbar.

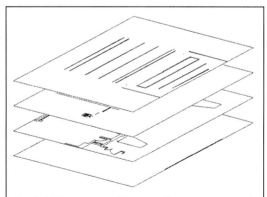

Fig 3-2 The Properties toolbar.

Layers are a very important part of AutoCAD and allow you to group items that belong together logically. You may assign a Colour and a Linetype to each layer. This helps you quickly identify each one. So, for instance, we would create separate Layers for the Theatre's groundplan, another for the set and another for lighting. This idea comes from the concept of clear acetate overlays used by architects

Fig 3-3 The concept of Layers allows separation of common information into groups. In manual drawings many layers of acetates would be placed over a common master drawing.

to show the electrical installation, furniture, lighting etc of a building on top of a floorplan or other drawing *Fig 3-3*.

In fact, Layers can be far more complicated than this and throughout the book, we will follow the CAD Standards of the Association of British Theatre Technicians (ABTT). This Standard defines Layer titles and colours as well as Linetypes, which are used to define the properties of objects in terms of their height above the stage, whether they are permanent or temporary structures etc as well as their classification in terms of group.

Embedded in the ABTT system is the idea of Parent and Child Layers. This also extends to Grand Children! The example below shows the Layers for Flying, which is colour coded green. Where possible standard colours available across most CAD programs have been used.

Layer 4 Flying	This is the Parent for all the Layers associated with Flying.
Layer 4a CW Bars	This is the Child Layer and the theatre's Counterweight bars would be drawn on this Layer.
Layer 4a CW Bars @CL	This is a Grandchild Layer and allows more, or alternative information to be shown.

The Layer shown 4a CW Bars @ CL has a short section of a bar shown at the Centre Line, which some people like to have on a drawing. Other Grandchildren of this Layer include:

4a CW Bars @Ends	Showing a short section of the bar at its extremities.
4a CW Bars @Gallery	Showing the position of the bar on the side it is operated from. This is for adding information such as what the bar contains.

In addition to help see them, all the bars, which are part of the Counterweight Layer group are in a different shade of green from the Parent Flying Layer.

As our Theatre progresses in its construction we will need to create Layers, otherwise this will be a very dull drawing to look at and rather difficult to read.

Open up the Theatre drawing you have created so far. Layer 0 is shown in the window of the Layers Toolbar. If you click on the drop down arrow to the right of the window of the Layers toolbar you will see that this is in fact the only Layer currently in this drawing. Layer 0 is the default Layer which is a part of any new drawing.

Creating Layers

Click on the Layer Properties Manager Icon and a new dialog box opens *Fig 3-4.*

Layer Properties Manager icon

As you can see the dialog box tells us that Layer 0 has the Continuous Linetype, again the default and is white (assuming you have a black drawing area) also the default.

The first new Layer we need to add is one for our Centre Line. This Layer will also have the Setting Line on it and is called 1A Datum

To create it just click on the New button in the dialog box and a new Layer appears below 0 titled Layer 1. As it is highlighted, you can rename it as above.

Layer Colours

The Datum Layer should be yellow so next click on the colour square, which is white and the Select Color dialog box is shown in *Fig 3-5.* Pick the yellow square and then OK. This will return you to the Layer Properties Manager where you can see your Datum Layer now has yellow assigned to it.

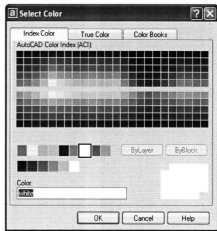

Fig 3-4 Layer Properties dialogue.　　*Fig 3-5 Layer Colour dialogue.*

Layer Linetypes

The next property we can assign here is the Linetype. Again click on the Linetype currently loaded (Continuous) and you are taken to another dialog box Select Linetypes *Fig 3-6*. As you can see the range is currently rather limited. What we need to do is load the Linetypes we need into this dialog box.

Click on Load and you will see a list of available Linetypes, together with a diagram of their appearance. *Fig 3-7*.

The Linetype we need is 'Phantom'. This is a long dash followed by two shorter ones. Click on the Linetype and you are returned to the previous dialog box. Both Continuous and Phantom are now loaded. Highlight Phantom by clicking on it then OK. You are returned to the Layer Properties Manager, and Phantom is now set as our LineType.

Fig 3-6 The Select Linetype dialog box showing AutoCAD's default LineType, Continuous.

Fig 3-7 The Load LineTypes dialog box showing some of the LineTypes available.

Layer LineWeight

Lastly we should look at LineWeight. LineWeight is a thickness applied to a line and has the same effect as using a 0.3 pen as opposed to our normal 0.1 pen when drawing on paper. This helps identify different parts of the drawing and certain Layers do need this extra property to be set up.

It should be noted that LineWeights are used to differentiate lines when they are plotted and once set are not generally used whilst drawing. This replaces an older system of assigning LineWeights to colours, which was limiting.

LineWeight sizes are real world sizes, showing the thickness a line will be when it is printed.

Although this particular Layer does not have a LineWeight we will set one up to see the effect. We can easily get rid of it when we need to.

Again click on the Default entry in the Layer's LineWeight Coloumn. The LineWeight dialog box appears *Fig 3-8*. LineWeights don't really show until about 0.30mm so select that.

Now we have set our Layer up, click OK at the bottom of the Layer Properties Manager. This returns you to the Drawing Screen.

If you now look at the other half of the toolbar, Properties, all the windows now have the word ByLayer in them together with small illustrations of the properties of the Layer that we have just created. ByLayer means that the property used is the one associated with the Layer by default. Of course you can use the drop downs to change the properties but generally speaking this is not encouraged as it works against the principals of using Standards.

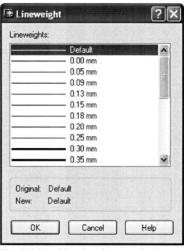

Fig 3-8 LineWeight selection dialogue.

Click on the drop down in the Layers toolbar and select 1A Datum to make it active and then draw the Setting Line. This runs parallel to the upstage edge of the Safety Curtain and extends across to the side border of the drawing

Your line should be yellow and in the Phantom linetype. It does however not appear to be any thicker than normal. This is because using LineWeight increases the redraw speed of a screen, so by default it is left off on the display. To turn it on click the LWT button on the Status Bar and your LineWeight should be obvious now, *Fig 3-9*. Because we don't actually want this LWT on this Layer return to the Layer Properties Manager and reset it to Default.

We now need to put our Centre Line into the right Layer. Click on it and it will change to a dashed line with three blue boxes (Grips) along it. Now select the 1A Datum Layer on the Layers toolbar and the line will take on the properties we have just set up. Hit Esc to clear the Grips.

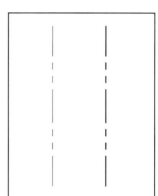

Fig 3-9 LineWeights in action. The line on the left has an LWT of 0 (the default). The line on the right has an LWT of .30mm and the LWT button on the Status bar is selected. LineWeights can be added to any Layer or object but are only active if the toggle is on.

LineType Scale

It may be that you cannot see the Linetype when in certain drawings, particularly ones the size of our groundplan. This may be because the LineType Scale is set at its default, which on a larger drawing gives the appearance of any LineType being Continuous. LineType Scale or LTS is the ratio between the dots, dashes and gaps in a LineType.

The LTS command is a global command. This means that all the LineTypes in a drawing will be changed to the new scale. To change the scale globally do this:

```
Type: LTS ↵
LTSCALE Enter new linetype scale factor
<1.0000>: 25 ↵
Regenerating model.
```

Try using our drawing scale in the first instance. Remember we should be able to distinguish the LineType both close up and when we have zoomed right out. This may mean we have to alter some linetypes individually.

Properties

To alter the properties of individual objects requires the use of the Properties Palette. Palettes are a new way of AutoCAD displaying certain dialog boxes. Palettes are more flexible than the old docked dialog boxes used prior to AutoCAD 2004. See the Palettes tips at end of chapter.

Properties Palette icon

To open the Properties Palette you can click on the Icon on the Standard Toolbar. Alternatively, a double click on an object will launch it. *Fig 3-10.*

There are several sections to this Palette. These alter according to what is selected. As we have a Line currently selected, the following categories are shown: General and Geometry. Use the scroll bar on the Palette if you can't see them all.

LineType Scale is in the first section,

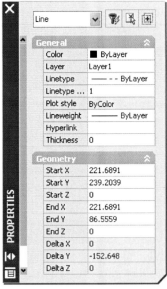
Fig 3-10 The Properties Palette.

General. This value Scale is set to 1. This seems odd until you fully understand the relationship between the Global Line Type Scale and an Objects.

To arrive at the LTS that is actually displayed, one scale is multiplied by the other, therefore in this case, Global LTS x Object LTs is 25 x 1 = 25. As a result, the line is displayed with an LTS of 25, which is what we want.

Altering either LTS will affect how the objects Linetype is displayed. Values greater than 1 give fewer repetitions of your Linetypes elements; less than 1 will give more but may seem to be a continuous line. The lines in *Fig 3-11* all have a global LTS of 25, but the Object LTS are from Left to Right 0.5, 1 and 2.

In the other properties box, under Geometry you will see several entries, which are actually coordinates. By changing the numerical value in these, you will change the object you have created. Alternatively, by selecting the Pick icon which appears in any of the windows you select, you can change that properties by moving your mouse around the drawing area. Any of these changes are updated in the Properties Palette. *Fig 3-12.*

Fig 3-11 LineType Scales from left to right LTS scales of 0.5, 1 (the default) and 2.

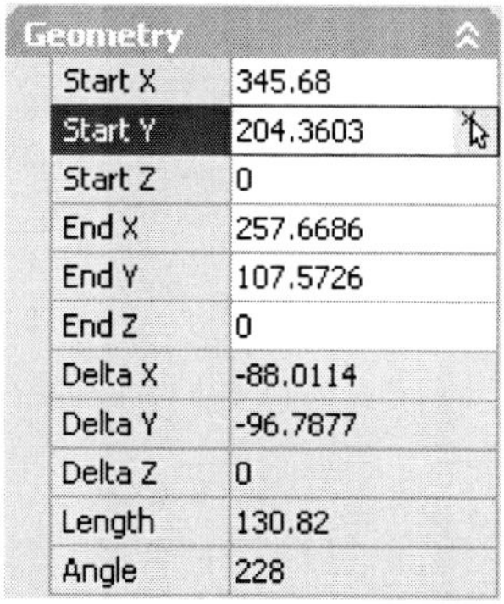

Geometry	
Start X	345.68
Start Y	204.3603
Start Z	0
End X	257.6686
End Y	107.5726
End Z	0
Delta X	-88.0114
Delta Y	-96.7877
Delta Z	0
Length	130.82
Angle	228

Fig 3-12 Moving the start point of a Line using the Properties Palette

Theatre Drawing 2

Before continuing the drawing let us create the Layers we will require in this section. Make sure you are on the right Layer as you draw by opening the Layers drop down and clicking the required Layer *Fig 3-13*. It can be changed later but this is tedious if a lot needs moving.

Layer Name	Colour	LineType	LineWeight
1b Structure - Walls	White	Continuous	.7mm
1b Structure - Doors	White	Continuous	.5mm
1d Orchestra Pit	White	Continuous	.7mm

1e Safety Curtain	White	ISO 03W100	.35mm
2a Stage Floor	Grey	Continuous	.7mm

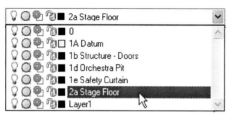

Fig 3-13 *Changing an object Layer using the Layers Toolbar drop down.*

Once you have done that, start to assign what we have drawn so far to the correct Layer. You can switch a layer off by clicking on the lightbulb in the Layers Window. This will cause the drop down to appear and from there, you can select which Layers to switch off. If a layer is off it disappears from the screen and therefore any objects on it cannot be selected.

We should have two Layers that have nothing on them. We will create our orchestra pit first, then add some doors on the stage so we can get on and off.

We need to define the edge of the stage first so make sure you are in Layer 2a Stage Floor. The edge of the Stage is curved so we will need to use the Arc command.

Arcs

There are seven parts of an Arc that are used to create them. Fortunately we only need to use three at a time *Fig 3-14.*

If you click Draw ➤ Arc you will see the range of creation options available. We will use the 3 Point method to create our stage edge and orchestra pit.

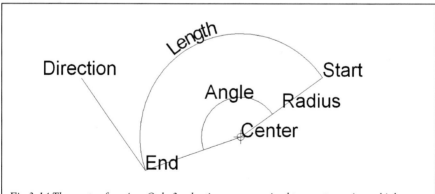

Fig 3-14 *The parts of an Arc. Only 3 selections are required to create an Arc, which ones depends on what you are trying to create and your personal preference.*

We need to use a construction line, which we will then delete, so follow these instructions:

```
Command: _line Specify first point:
```
Pick the Mid of the downstage side of the safety curtain

```
Specify next point or [Undo]: @0,-1200 ⏎
Specify next point or [Undo]: ⏎
```
Next start the 3 Point Arc command.

Either Click Draw ➤ Arc ➤ 3 Point

or Click the Arc Icon on the Draw Toolbar

or Type Arc ⏎ at the Command Line.

Arc icon

```
Command: _arc Specify start point of arc
or [Center]:
```
Pick the DS Endpoint of the short line extending out from the Safety Curtain ⏎

```
Specify second point of arc or [Center/End]:
```
Pick the Endpoint of the construction line we just drew

```
Specify end point of arc:
```
Pick the equivalent Endpoint to our first one on the opposite side of the stage.

Fig 3- 15 shows what you should have drawn. You can now delete the construction line.

Next, Offset the Arc by 2000 to create the pit itself. Move the new Arc onto the right Layer and then finish the pit by joining the ends of the two Arcs to create *Fig 3-16.*

Fig 3-15 Theatre Apron added, showing construction line. Note that this is on the Floor Layer.

The 3 Point Arc creation method is unique in one important factor. It can be drawn in either clock or anti clockwise directions. All other Arcs can only be created running anti clockwise.

By default the Arc Icon is set to 3

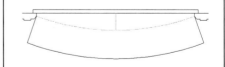

Fig 3-16 Orchestra pit now added on its own layer.

Point so it is generally best to go via the Menu when selecting your way of drawing Arcs.

Make Layer 1b Structure – Doors current. Then Zoom into the DSL area of the theatre, around the prompt corner.

We need to draw a line 2000 up stage across the wall thickness then Offset it and finally Trim it to create a door opening. Make sure Ortho is on so your lines are straight.

```
Command: _line Specify first point:
```
Pick the inside corner of the wall DSL ⏎
```
Specify next point or [Undo]: ⏎
```
Restart the Line Command
```
Command:LINE Specify first point: @0,2000
Specify next point or [Undo]:
```
Pick the outside edge of the wall ⏎
```
Specify next point or [Undo]: ⏎
Command: offset
Specify offset distance or [Through]
<2000.0000>: 1200
Select object to offset or <exit>:
```
Pick the Line we just created ⏎
```
Specify point on side to offset:
```
Pick the upstage side
```
Select object to
offset or <exit>: ⏎
```
This produces *Fig 3-17.*

Trim

Now we have defined the door we need to cut a hole in the wall to get through it. Trim uses one object as a cutting edge. Any line intersecting this edge can then be cut back to it.

We can pick two edges in this case and remove the Line between

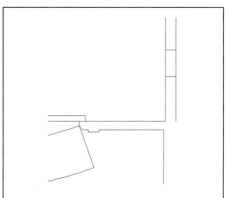

Fig 3-17 Defining the position of the first doorway.

them creating our door opening.

Either Click Modify ➤ Trim

or Click the Trim Icon on the ModifyToolbar

or Type Trim ↵ at the Command Line.

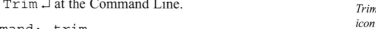

```
Command: trim
Current settings: Projection=UCS,
Edge=Extend
Select cutting edges ...
Select objects: 1 found
```

Pick one of the lines we just created

```
Select objects: 1 found, 2 total
```

Pick the other one

```
Select objects: ↵
Select object to trim or shift-select to
extend or [Project/Edge/Undo]:
```

Pick a line between the two cutting edges we have just defined

```
Select object to trim or shift-select to
extend or [Project/Edge/Undo]:
```

Pick the other line ↵

```
Select object to trim
or shift-select to
extend or [Project/
Edge/Undo]: ↵
```

And here is what you should now have *Fig 3-18.*

Creating a Door

Firstly ensure you are on the 1b Structure – Doors layer.

Now zoom right in to the doorway we have just created. What we are going to do is create a door, showing it in both its open and closed positions and

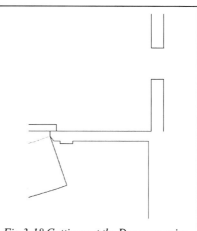

Fig 3-18 Cutting out the Doorway using Trim.

the arc of the door's swing.

We will use Rectangle, Rotate and the Start, End, Angle Arc Commands. First the door using Rectangle.

```
Command: _rectang
Specify first corner point or [Chamfer/
Elevation/Fillet/Thickness/Width]:
```

Pick the bottom left corner of the doorway

```
Specify other corner point or [Dimensions]:
@50,1200 ↵
```

Note that we are using a relative coordinate to create the door.
We will now repeat the Rectangle drawing over the one we have just created. This allows us to Rotate only one copy of the door leaving the other in place.

```
Command:RECTANG
Specify first corner point or [Chamfer/
Elevation/Fillet/Thickness/Width]:
```

Pick a corner of the door

```
Specify other corner point or [Dimensions]:
```

Using an Osnap pick the diagonally opposite corner

Rotate

To use the Rotate command you need to specify what it is you wish to rotate and most importantly the centre point about which it revolves. Inaccurate placement of the centre point will lead to surprising and unintended results. Using Osnaps will help in getting this right.

The angle of rotation can be defined in three ways, via the mouse movement, by inputting a numerical value or by referencing to an existing object you want to align to.

We will repeat creating our open door with each method. *Fig 3-19* shows what we are aiming to create.

Start Rotate by either

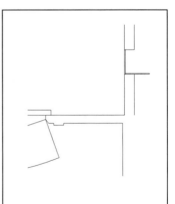

Fig 3-19 Door added and shown in both open and closed positions.

Clicking Modify ➤ Rotate

or Click the Rotate Icon on the ModifyToolbar

or Type Rotate ⏎ at the Command Line.

Rotate icon

The Mouse Method

```
Command: _rotate
Current positive angle in UCS:
ANGDIR=counterclockwise   ANGBASE=0
```

Pick the door Rectangle

```
Select objects: 1 found
Select objects: ⏎
Specify base point:
```

Pick the bottom right corner of the door.

```
Specify rotation angle or [Reference]:
```

Now move the mouse. We want a rotation of 90° to the right. If you have Ortho on this is easy. Just move the mouse straight down, wait a second and you'll see the door appear in the right place, opening down and offstage.

If you don't have Ortho on, you will find it quite difficult to get this right but experiment. See what happens if you shorten the rubberband that appears and also try zooming in using the mouse's middle wheel.

In both cases, click when your door is in the right position.

Numeric Value Method

Undo your last rotation, then start rotate again. The door should end up in the same place so try a value and see what you get. Remember in AutoCAD angles run anti clockwise with 0° at 3 o'clock.

The correct inputs are:

```
Command: _rotate
Current positive angle in UCS:
ANGDIR=counterclockwise   ANGBASE=0
```

Once the command has started pick the same objects and base point for rotation.

```
Select objects: 1 found
Select objects: ⏎
Specify base point:
```

```
Specify rotation angle or [Reference]: -90
```

The correct value to get the door open is –90. This is because we are going clockwise and therefore against normal rotation, hence it is a minus figure.

Try doing this with a variety of positive and negative values and see what you get. When you have finished experimenting undo all you have done ready for the next method.

Reference Method

For this method you need an object with which to line up. In this case, it is the downstage side of the doorway. The secret of this method is in the order of picks, which is easy to forget, as I know only too well.

Start the command as before, picking the door and rotation base point. Then follow this

```
Specify rotation angle or [Reference]: r
Specify the reference angle <0>:
```

Pick your original base point again

```
Specify second point:
```

Pick the top right corner of the door (directly above the base point)
Specify the new angle:
Pick the offstage bottom corner of the doorway.
The order of Picks and result is shown in *Fig 3-20*.

Creating the door arc

As noted above we will use the SEA (Start, End, Angle) method. Before drawing anything let us work through the methodology of arc creation.

Firstly, it is important to remember that Arcs, apart from the 3 Point, run anti clockwise. This is vital to understand, especially when defining your Start and End points.

Secondly the angle is our included angle and therefore does not relate to our polar coordinate angles discussed in Chapter 2

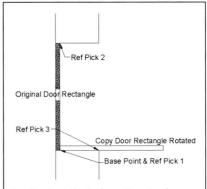

Fig 3-20 Method of creating the door using the Rotate using a Reference method.

Pick Draw ➤ Arc ➤ Start, End, Angle

```
Command: _arc Specify start point of arc or
[Center]:
```

Pick the top right corner of the open door (the horizontal one)

```
Specify second point of arc or [Center/End]:
_e
```

Specify end point of arc:

Pick the equivalent point on our shut (vertical) door

```
Specify center point of arc or [Angle/
Direction/Radius]: _a Specify included angle:
90 ↵
```

You should have a result as in *Fig 3-21*.

Now we have a door we can copy it and move it wherever we like. I have four doors on my stage but you can add as many or few as you like. Some of them may need rotating unless you want the doors opening onstage.

Remember when you have placed the doors to trim back the wall to create the opening.

Next we should draw in the dock doors upstage right. First though, draw the two lines required to finish the doorway here.

Create two rectangles to fill in the gap. They should be 1500 wide by 250 deep, although the thickness isn't important. Make sure they are on the inside of the wall so they can be opened as far as possible.

Using Osnaps, draw two more rectangles over the first two (or just copy them over each other) and, using Rotate, open the doors as far as possible. You'll find the right hand door will open flush to the back wall but the left hand door does not. Does this sound familiar to anyone?

Once your doors are open again, we will add in their Arcs, this time using the Start, Center, End method of Arc creation.

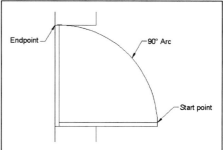

Fig 3-21 Door swing added in. It is important to add these details to avoid storage problems in a crowded wing. Fortunately this door opens off stage.

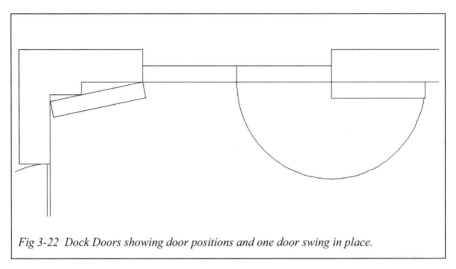

Fig 3-22 Dock Doors showing door positions and one door swing in place.

We will start with the right hand door. Remembering the direction that our Arcs run, start the command using Draw ➤ Arc ➤ Start, Center, End

> Command: _arc Specify start point of arc or [Center]:

Pick the point where the two shut doors meet.

> Specify second point of arc or [Center/End]:
> _c Specify center point of arc:

This is the same point as you rotated the doors around when you opened them

> Specify end point of arc or [Angle/chord Length]:

Pick the onstage end of the door

Fig 3-22 shows the result. If you look carefully, the Arc does not actually describe the full extent of the door opening, even if you used Osnaps.

We can rectify this using the Grips, the little blue boxes that appeared when we were changing properties.

Grips

Grips have simple editing functions, Stretch, Move, Rotate, Scale and Mirror. They are accessed by firstly picking the Grip you need to use. It will change to a red box, called the hot grip and you will be in Stretch mode. By hitting the spacebar, you can cycle through the available commands.

Stretch is however, what we need, so make the Grip hot where the Arc does not reach the end of the door and drag it along until it does. Hit ESC to clear the Grips. You can zoom in for a closer look and use the Endpoint Osnap for accuracy.

Once this door is complete, create the Arc for the other door, editing it if necessary with the Grips.

The result of all our efforts thus far is shown in *Fig 3-23*.

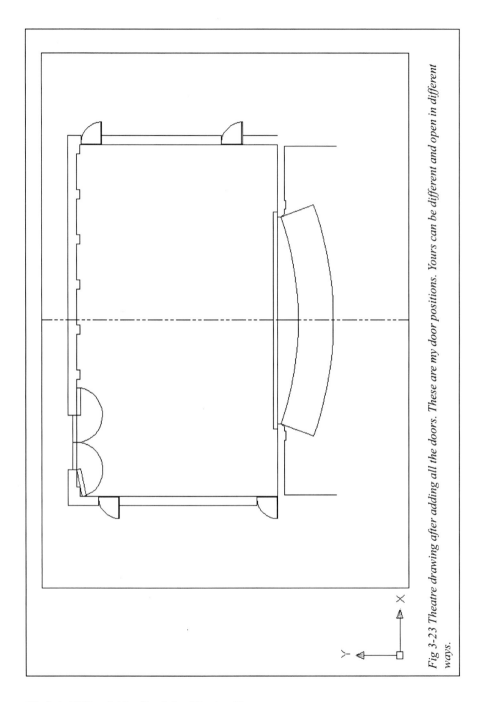

Fig 3-23 Theatre drawing after adding all the doors. These are my door positions. Yours can be different and open in different ways.

Palettes

Fig B3-1 The Properties Palette docked.

Palettes are a new concept to AutoCAD, introduced in 2004. On the Standard Toolbar are 3 Icons, Properties, DesignCenter and a new one, the Tools Palette.

Tip!

In previous versions when you opened either of the first two as a default, they floated in the Drawing Area. Alternatively, you could dock them wherever you wanted them *Fig B3-1.*

Palettes do the same but with the important addition of the blue strip down the left hand side. This adds the possibility to close the palette when you don't need, thus maintaining the maximum Drawing Area or automatically hiding whenever you move the mouse away from it.

Fig B3-2. These options are available via the Properties sib menu accesses via the icon at the very bottom of the blue bar.

The third Palette is the Tool Palette *Fig B3-3* As you can see on the standard Tool Palette there are three tabs: two are Hatches and the other holds a combination of Hatches and Blocks (see Chapter 6).

Each of these tabs is regarded by AutoCAD as a Tool Palette within the Tool Palette Window. The Hatches and Blocks are the Tools, which can be dragged and dropped into a drawing. As such, it is not expected that anyone

Fig B3-2 Floating Properties Palette

will use the Tool Palette Window as it is. They are designed to be customised by each user so that contain the items they would use most.

Creating a custom Tool Palette/tab will be discussed in Chapter 6 when we will also look at the AutoCAD DesignCenter.

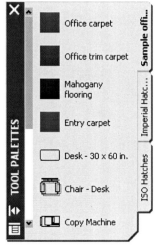

Fig B3-3 The Tool Palette Window. Each tab is a Tool Palette containing customisable items such as Hatches, Blocks, etc.

4 FINISHING THE THEATRE'S STRUCTURE

Fly Floors

In drawing the Fly Floors or Galleries as they are referred to in the ABTT CAD Standards, we need to create another new Layer. As these are permanent features above 1800mm they used a dashed line as their LineType.

1c Galleries   Colour: White   LineType: 03W100   LWT: 0.5

As shown in *Fig 4-1* add a fly floor each side, the stage left one being much wider than Stage right, which is 2000mm wide. Next add a perch each side; they are accessed via cat ladders so draw those in, using the Polygon to make the square of the hatchway and Lines and Circles (see later in this chapter), trimmed as necessary. The detail is shown in *Fig 4-2*.

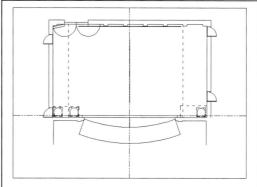

Fig 4-1 Flyfloors and perches added to each side.

Part of the area we need to draw associated with the Fly floor is the Counterweight cradles. Over any doorways we can assume that double purchase cradles are used and do not extend below the fly floor, the rest are single purchase and reach the floor. These will obviously affect the area that can be used on stage so need to be shown.

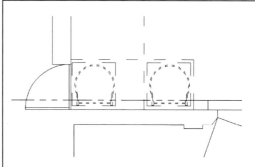

Fig 4-2 Detail for creating Cat ladders up to the perches.

Again, this is a simple task using lines, but to draw the lines we will use another tool called Polar Tracking.

Polar Tracking

Polar tracking allows us to reference a point by floating the mouse over it to acquire it, then we can draw intersections from the two points.

Make sure you are on the right Layer, which should be:

Layer 4a CW Cradles   Colour: Green Linetype: Continuous   LWT : 0.5

Switch on Polar Tracking, either by clicking the POLAR button on the Status bar or by using F10. Start your line on the SL wall where your counterweight would reach the floor. In my drawing, there is a doorway in the USL corner so I am using the DS edge of the doorframe.

I have set the depth of the Cradles at 750mm so start the Line command:

```
Command: _line Specify first point:
Specify next point or [Undo]: @ -750,0
```

Now move your mouse downstage. You will see a tooltip appear by your crosshairs, showing the distance from the last point and the angle. If you move the mouse around, you will notice it snaps and the tooltip appears every 90° *Fig 4-3*. This is the default and can be changed via the settings dialog box which is easily reached by right clicking on the Polar button. Once in the dialog box you can change the set angles by clicking the Additional Angles box and adding them in the window below.

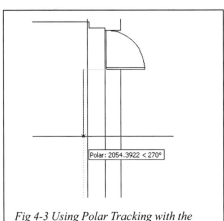

Fig 4-3 Using Polar Tracking with the tooltip activated.

Back to the drawing: move the mouse down until you are about level with where you want this line to end. Zoom in using your mouse wheel and then move the mouse over the point on the wall, or doorframe, in my case, you want the line to end at. As you hover the mouse over the point, the Osnap will appear in another tool tip *Fig 4-4*.

Do not click!

Instead, move the mouse back to join the vertical line and when you meet it in line with the Endpoint you just picked up left click *Fig 4-5*. You need to be careful here to keep the lines straight as using Polar turns off Ortho. Now click back at the Endpoint and the enclosure for your cradles is complete.

My next set of single purchase cradles run from the downstage side of another door to the perch. With Polar Tracking still on, start the Line command and pick the doors DS edge, finding an endpoint. Now move your mouse onstage and the Polar tooltip will appear. As we noted above, the distance is shown as well as the angle.

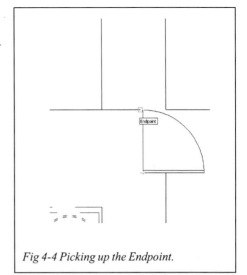

Fig 4-4 Picking up the Endpoint.

When the tooltip shows that you are 750mm away from the start point you could click to create the line, however you may find it tricky to be absolutely accurate. Instead, just type 750 ↵ and your Line will be created. Using Polar tracking, if you know both the angle and the distance you only need to actually enter the distance. This is called DDE - Direct Distance Entry.

The command line looks like this:

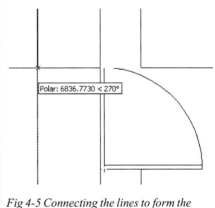

Fig 4-5 Connecting the lines to form the Counterweight Cages.

```
Command: _line
Specify first point:
Specify next point or [Undo]: 750 ↵
Specify next point or [Undo]:
```
I used Nearest on the perch directly below
```
Specify next point or [Close/Undo]: ↵
```

Circles

Circles are very simple to create in AutoCAD, usually requiring a centre point and either a radius or diameter.

There are other tools but generally the two above are the ones you will use the most. In any case let's go through them.

On the default AutoCAD template, start the Circle command by one of the usual methods.

Either Click the Circle Icon on the Draw Toolbar

or Type Circle ⌐ at the Command Line.

Circle icon

If you use the Draw ➤ Circle route then you need to make your choice of creation method first, so stick to the two alternatives above first time round.

On the command line you should see:

```
Command: _circle Specify center point for
circle or [3P/2P/Ttr (tan tan radius)]:
```

Pick a point (or enter a coordinate)

```
Specify radius of circle or [Diameter]:
```

You have three choices here:

1 Move the mouse and watch a Circle pull out from the centre point. Click when it is the right size *Fig 4-6*

2 Enter a value for the radius and hit ⌐

3 Type D and enter a diameter value then ⌐

Restart the Circle command and this time we'll define our Circle using two points

```
Command: CIRCLE
Specify first end point
of circle's diameter:
Specify center point for
circle or [3P/2P/Ttr
(tan tan radius)]: 2p ⌐
```

Specify first end point of circle's diameter.

Pick a point on the first Circle you created using Osnap, such as the Quadrant (a diamond shaped marker). This allows us to see how this method works.

```
Specify second end point
```

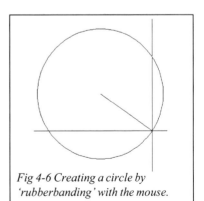

Fig 4-6 Creating a circle by 'rubberbanding' with the mouse.

```
of circle's
diameter:
```
Pick a point or enter a relative or Polar coordinate to define the other end of the circles diameter *Fig 4-7.*

3 Point defines our circle using 3 picks or coordinates. Whilst the last two methods need objects to relate to, to produce Tangents, in the case of Tan, Tan, Radius with a numeric value.

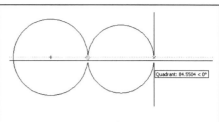

Fig 4-7 Creating a circle using 2 Points to define a diameter.

Our Theatre is lucky enough to have an 8 metre revolve, as, in a minute we are going to sheet over our revolve until we need it I think we should place it on one of the Subfloor Layers. We would move it when it was used for a show. Create this Layer to place our Revolve on:

3d Subfloor – Revolve, Colour; Red, Linetype; ISO W2W100, LWT;.35mm

Then draw the revolve with its centre 5475mm upstage from the back of the Iron. Chose the creation method you feel most comfortable with. Generally speaking this is dependent on whether you think in radii or diameters. It is easy to put your diameter in when AutoCAD requests the radius, so don't be too surprised when it is considerably larger than you intended!

Next we want to add the construction detail if the revolve in on a new Layer. Create a new Layer with the same properties as the current Revolve one; just change the name to reflect the differences.

Ellipse and Ellipse Arc

Although we don't require an Ellipse in the drawing we will use the Ellipse Arc to create the circle front. Both use common commands so we will start by looking at the basic Ellipse.

With Ellipses and Ellipse Arc, it is important to know which way you want your major axis to run. That is the wider part of the object.

Let us have a look at the command sequence for creating an Ellipse.

Either Click Draw ➢ Ellipse

Click the Ellipse Icon on the Draw Toolbar

or Type ellipse ↵ at the Command Line

Ellipse icon

```
Command: _ellipse
```

```
Specify axis endpoint of ellipse or [Arc/
Center]:
```
Pick a point or enter a coordinate
```
Specify other endpoint of axis: @0,-200 ↵
Specify distance to other axis or [Rotation]:
200
```
You will have created an Ellipse as shown in *Fig 4-8*.

You may be confused because we have apparently entered a dimension of 200 twice. It is perhaps easier then to think of the first two points you are asked for as a diameter, whilst the second distance is a radius.

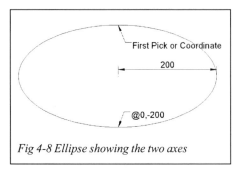
Fig 4-8 Ellipse showing the two axes

To place your Ellipse accurately use the following sequence. It will create the same sized ellipse as before:
```
Command: _ellipse
Specify axis endpoint of ellipse or [Arc/
Center]: c ↵
Specify center of ellipse:
```
Pick a point or enter a coordinate.
```
Specify endpoint of axis: @0,100 ↵
```
This time you are specifying a radius
```
Specify distance to other axis or [Rotation]:
200 ↵
```
Finally we will create an Ellipse using the Rotation option.
```
Command: _ellipse
Specify axis endpoint of ellipse or [Arc/
Center]:
```
Pick a point or enter a coordinate
```
Specify other endpoint of axis: @0,100 ↵
Specify distance to other axis or [Rotation]:
r ↵
```
Specify rotation around major axis:

Moving the mouse around will gives the appearance of the Ellipse spinning along the first axis you have defined. Left click when it is at the size you need.

Ellipse arc allows you to create an Arc from an Ellipse. As you will see this is a useful command when creating a deep Arc (a bit like the top end of an egg).

On your theatre drawing, create another new Layer

1f Auditorium – Circle   Colour: White   Linetype: 03W100 LWT 0.5

Follow the commands below to create our circle. Much of the process is the same as creating an ordinary Ellipse.

```
Command: _ellipse
Specify axis endpoint of ellipse or [Arc/
Center]: _a
Specify axis endpoint of elliptical arc or
[Center]: c
Specify center of elliptical arc:
```

Pick the Midpoint on the downstage side of the safety curtain

```
Specify endpoint of axis: @0,-10000
Specify distance to other axis or [Rotation]:
```

Pick the off-stage side of the column on the auditorium side of the prosc. wall. See figure 4-12 for what you should end up with.

```
Specify start angle or [Parameter]:
```

Pick the same point

```
Specify end angle or [Parameter/Included
angle]:
```

Pick the equivalent point on the other side of the Prosc.

As with anything involving Arcs, remember that Arcs run anti clockwise so the order of picking is important. Once you have created the Circle offset the Ellipse arcs by 50 to give it a bit of thickness.

The Ellipse Arc extends beyond our border so we need to trim it. I prefer to leave a bit of space around the drawing. To do this, Offset the drawing border by 100 inside and use that to trim back the circle. We can delete it later, when we have tidied up any other objects crossing this inner border.

Whilst we are up in the circle, let us look at a couple of other editing tools.

Chamfer and Fillet
Both Icons for Chamfer and Fillet look very similar, particularly if your screen

resolution is high and your icons small. Use the tooltips to make sure until you are confident which one is which (Chamfer is the top one). There is also a problem, I find, of remembering which command produces which result.

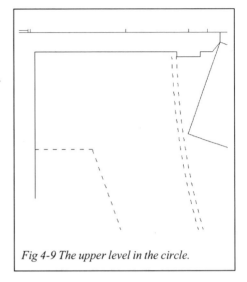

We will create another part of the auditorium at circle level by creating a level behind where our front row of seats will be. Using Line create the following:

```
Command: _line
Specify first point:
```
On Auditorium left pick the corner

Fig 4-9 The upper level in the circle.

of the Auditorium and Prosc Walls.
```
Specify next point or [Undo]: ↵
```
Restart the Line command
```
Command: LINE
Specify first point: @0,-2000 ↵
Specify next point or [Undo]: @1200,0 ↵
Specify next point or [Undo]: @5350<290 ↵
Specify next point or [Close/Undo]: ↵
```
Fig 4-9 shows what you have drawn.

Chamfer

Chamfer shaves a corner in a straight line, according to a pair of distances you specify. To start this command

Either Click Modify ➢ Chamfer

Click the Chamfer Icon on the ModifyToolbar

or Type chamfer ↵ at the Command Line

Chamfer icon

Follow these commands:
```
Command: _chamfer
(TRIM mode) Current chamfer Dist1 = 0.0000,
Dist2 = 0.0000
```

```
Select first line or
[Polyline/Distance/
Angle/Trim/Method/
mUltiple]: d ↵
Specify first
chamfer distance
<0.0000>: 200 ↵
Specify second
chamfer distance
<200.0000>: ↵
Select first line or
[Polyline/Distance/
Angle/Trim/Method/
mUltiple]:
```

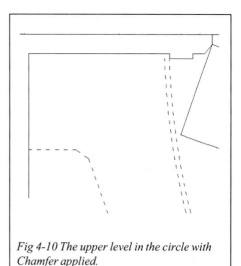

Fig 4-10 The upper level in the circle with Chamfer applied.

Select either line

```
Select second line:
```

Pick the other one. The result you should have is shown in *Fig 4-10*

The Distance we created is the distance from the corner where the two lines meet. If you have two different distances then order of selection becomes vital.

Try applying to differing values to the first and second lines and applying the Fillet. Undo this and then repeat the Fillet command but this time pick the lines in the opposite order and note the result, which will be different from the first time.

Fillet

Fillet will round off a corner and this is what we want to create for the drawing. Obviously if you are happy with the Chamfer, keep that.

Undo your Chamfers so the lines meet cleanly then open the Fillet command by one of the usual methods.

Fillet icon

Either Click Modify ➢ Fillet

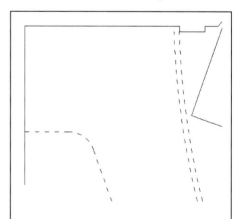

Fig 4-11 The upper level in the circle with Fillet applied.

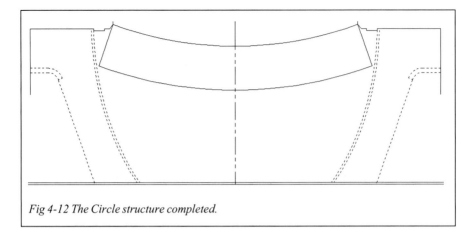

Fig 4-12 The Circle structure completed.

Click the Fillet Icon on the ModifyToolbar

or Type fillet ↵ at the Command Line

```
Command: _fillet
Current settings: Mode = TRIM, Radius =
0.0000
Select first object or [Polyline/Radius/Trim/
mUltiple]: r ↵
Specify fillet radius <0.0000>: 500 ↵
Select first object or [Polyline/Radius/Trim/
mUltiple]:
Select second object:
```

Again, pick both lines to produce *Fig 4-11*.

To complete the structure of the circle I've added a step to get from the top level of the Circle down using an Offset by 200 as shown and tidied up as required. Finally, Mirror what you have drawn to create the other side of the circle. *Fig 4-12*.

Polygon

We will move back on stage now to create the underlying structure of the revolve. A Polygon in AutoCAD is an object with between 3 and 1024 equal sides.

We will assume the revolve is built with 'pieces of pie' so that each section is triangle, which is then sheeted to create the disc.

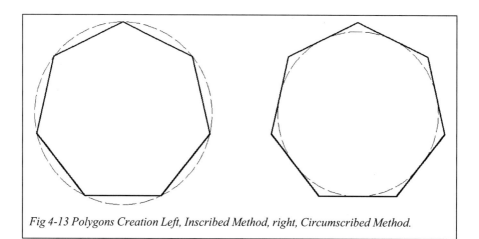

Fig 4-13 Polygons Creation Left, Inscribed Method, right, Circumscribed Method.

To create the revolve's substructure, we will use a Polygon for the outside of the frames. There are two methods of creating a Polygon: both include the creation of a circle which is never seen.

The Inscribed Circle method will leave you with a Polygon whose points touch the circle's circumference and so is inside the circle.

The other method Circumscribed Circle, is outside the defining circle with the mid point of each edge of the polygon touching the circumference. The differences between both methods are shown in *Fig 4-13*. Alternatively of course you can use the mouse to create the Polygon.

Before adding the construction detail, create a new Layer to place the drawing on:

3d Subfloor-Revolove Substructure Colour; Red Linetype; ISO W2W100 LWT; .35mm

Our revolve is built in 12 sections, so start the Polygon command with any of the usual alternatives:

Either Click Draw ➢ Polygon

Click the Polygon Icon on the Draw Toolbar

or Type polygon ↵ at the Command Line.

```
Command: polygon
Enter number of sides <4>: 12
Specify center of polygon or [Edge]:
```

Use the Center Osnap of the circle as the centre of the Polygon

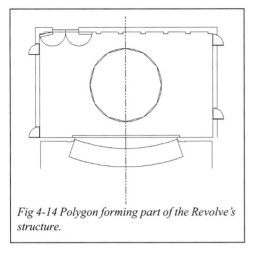

Fig 4-14 Polygon forming part of the Revolve's structure.

Enter an option
[Inscribed in
circle/
Circumscribed about
circle] <I>: ↵
Specify radius of
circle: 4000 ↵

You should now have a Polygon that sits inside the revolve's circle. Repeat the command, this time using the Circumscribed method to see the difference.

We will come back and look at adding the lines to create the wedges of the revolve in a second *Fig 4-14*.

Polylines

When we look at all the types of bars we would have in a theatre, they usually have a diameter of 48.4mm, assuming we are using standard scaffolding. It would be useful to represent this on our groundplan to give a true representation of the space they take up.

LineWeights are not suitable for this job, instead we will use a special kind of line called a Polyline.

Fig 4-15 Polyline Shapes.

Polylines have several attributes that ordinary lines do not have. The width of a Polyline can be varied, which means it can create not only thick lines but tapering ones as well.

Polylines are not only lines but Arcs as well, again the arcs can have width. You can switch between Arcs and Lines, all with different widths during one Polyline command. Lastly a series of Polylines created in a single command become one object once the command is finished.

We have already met a type of Polyline – the Rectangle. If you draw a rectangle using Lines, each line is individual. A Rectangle on the other hand is one object.

Lets draw some simple shapes to demonstrate the Polylines tricks. Use a new sheet for this *Fig 4-15*.

Polyline icon.

Start the Polyline command by either

Click Draw ➤ Polyline

Click the Polyline Icon on the Draw Toolbar

or Type pline ↵ at the Command Line

Firstly we'll draw the arrow on the left.

```
Command: PLINE
Specify start point: 125,50
Current line-width is 0.0000
Specify next point or [Arc/Halfwidth/Length/
Undo/Width] :w ↵

Specify starting width <0.0000>:50 ↵
Specify ending width <50.0000>:10 ↵
Specify next point or [Arc/Halfwidth/Length/
Undo/Width] :@0,150 ↵
Specify next point or [Arc/Halfwidth/Length/
Undo/Width] : ↵
```

This draws the tail of the arrow

```
Specify next point or [Arc/Close/Halfwidth/
Length/Undo/Width] :w ↵
Specify starting width <10.0000>: 75 ↵
Specify ending width <75.0000>: 0 ↵
Specify next point or [Arc/Close/Halfwidth/
Length/Undo/Width] : @0,100 ↵
```

```
Specify next point or [Arc/Close/Halfwidth/
Length/Undo/Width]: ↵
```

This completes the arrow. Next we'll draw the circular arrow. This time the line is one width, but the arrowhead is also an Arc.

```
Command: _pline
Specify start point: 375,185 ↵
Current line-width is 0.0000
Specify next point or [Arc/Halfwidth/Length/
Undo/Width]: a ↵
Specify endpoint of arc or [Angle/CEnter/
Direction/Halfwidth/Line/Radius/Second pt/
Undo/Width]:w ↵
Specify starting width <0.0000>: 10 ↵
Specify ending width <10.0000>: ↵
Specify endpoint of arc or [Angle/CEnter/
Direction/Halfwidth/Line/Radius/Second pt/
Undo/Width]:354,125 ↵
Specify endpoint of arc or [Angle/CEnter/
CLose/Direction/Halfwidth/Line/Radius/Second
pt/Undo/Width]: w ↵
Specify starting width <10.0000>: 30 ↵
Specify ending width <30.0000>: 0 ↵
Specify endpoint of arc or [Angle/CEnter/
CLose/Direction/Halfwidth/Line/Radius/Second
pt/Undo/Width]:
```

Use the start point of the arc and ↵
Lastly we'll draw the wavy line

```
Command: _pline
Specify start point: 450,50 ↵
Current line-width is 0.0000
Specify next point or [Arc/Halfwidth/Length/
Undo/Width]: a ↵
Specify endpoint of arc or
[Angle/CEnter/Direction/Halfwidth/Line/
Radius/Second pt/Undo/Width]: a ↵
```

```
Specify included angle: 180° ↵
Specify endpoint of arc or [CEnter/Radius]:
@0,50 ↵
Specify endpoint of arc or
[Angle/CEnter/CLose/Direction/Halfwidth/Line/
Radius/Second pt/Undo/Width]: @0,50 ↵
Specify endpoint of arc or
[Angle/CEnter/CLose/Direction/Halfwidth/Line/
Radius/Second pt/Undo/Width]: @0,50 ↵
Specify endpoint of arc or
[Angle/CEnter/CLose/Direction/Halfwidth/Line/
Radius/Second pt/Undo/Width]: @0,50 ↵
```
This creates the vertical wavy line
```
Specify endpoint of arc or
[Angle/CEnter/CLose/Direction/Halfwidth/Line/
Radius/Second pt/Undo/Width]: L
```
We have now switched out of Arc mode and back to Line.
```
Specify next point or [Arc/Close/Halfwidth/
Length/Undo/Width]: h ↵
Specify starting half-width <0.0000>: ↵
Specify ending half-width <0.0000>: 10 ↵
Specify next point or [Arc/Close/Halfwidth/
Length/Undo/Width]: @75,0 ↵
Specify next point or [Arc/Close/Halfwidth/
Length/Undo/Width]: ↵
```

If at any time you have clicked on any of the objects we have created you will see that they are in fact one object.

As noted above the width of a Polyline is a true width that will scale correctly when plotted and is the right size when onscreen.

Splines

Splines are a series of curves, defined by points picked by the user. They are actually non-uniform rational B-spline (NURBS) curves. There – I bet that explains everything! For the non-technical amongst us this means that as you pick your points the Spline command adapts the curves to accommodate the shape you are defining.

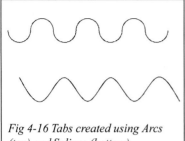

Fig 4-16 Tabs created using Arcs (top) and Splines (bottom).

Splines are the ideal tool for drawing any kind of cloth or material that has fullness in it. They are more flexible than using a series of Arcs or Polyline Arcs. Let's create two sets of Tabs, one created using Arcs, the other with Splines.

Using the default Drawing Sheet, set Grid and Snap to 25 and turn them on.

Start the Arc command picking the most left hand Grid/Snap on the second row. As we are using the 3 point method Snap on the point one across and one down, then one more across and one up so it is in line with the start point. Now restart the Arc, starting at the last Snap – this time go one up and one across, then one down and one across. You should now have *Fig 4-16*. Repeat this so you have at least four arcs across the screen.

Reset Snap to 50 to draw the Spline.

Now start the Spline command by

Clicking Draw ➢ Spline

Or Click the Spline Icon on the Draw Toolbar

or Type `spline` ↵ at the Command Line

Repeat the sequence as above, below the Arcs. The Spline command continues until you choose to stop it. Once you have reached the final Snap, there is the chance to use an existing tangent; just hit ↵ three times to end the command.

Spline icon.

The Spline will always pass through any points you pick so free flowing, complex shapes can be created using this method.

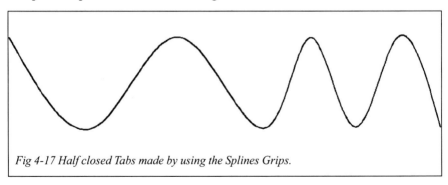

Fig 4-17 Half closed Tabs made by using the Splines Grips.

Now which you prefer as your tabs is a matter of choice and obviously, a different Snap or way of specifying your curves may give a better result. In using the Spline though, we have only started the command once, which is an advantage as far as I'm concerned. Also using the Spline it is easier, for instance, to indicate closed or partly closed tabs etc. *Fig 4-17*.

See Tips at end of chapter.

Donuts

Donuts are another way to draw circles, the difference being that this tool is designed to draw rings, hence their name.

To start with, Click Draw ➤ Donut

or Type donut ↵ at the Command Line.

```
Command: donut
Specify inside diameter of donut <0.5000>:500 ↵
Specify outside diameter of donut
<1.0000>:1000 ↵
Specify center of donut or <exit>:
```

Click or input a coordinate (if you use a coordinate hit ↵)

```
Specify center of donut or <exit>: ¿
```

Or keep dropping Donuts where you want them. Press ↵ when you want to end the command.

This will draw a ring. If you set the inside diameter to 0 then you will draw a solid disc. This is a good tool to show the bottom of booms or scaffolding.

Start the command again, this time give the inside diameter a value of 0 and the outside diameter a value of 48.4

Now place your booms onto the drawing. I have put one in each side of the prosc, I'll add a few later when we have more structure. You'll need a new Layer for these which is:

Fig 4-18 Donuts – Left a 48.4 mm Donut with no internal diameter. Right 100mm outer, 48.4mm internal diameter. These could represent booms with and without a scaffolding foot.

5a FOH LX Booms, Colour Cyan, Linetype Continuous, LWT 0.

You can see that using Donuts gives an accurate representation of the diameter of a boom, albeit in a 2-Dimensional representation. If your booms had circular feet on them you could show that by giving an inside diameter of 48 and an outside diameter of 100 *Fig 4-18*.

Points

Points are a different type of drawing object. To use Points you must firstly set the Point Style. Like LTS this is a global setting. This means that if you have previously used Points in a drawing, then change the style, every Point is updated to your new style.

In the theatre realm Points could be used to indicate rigging points for chain hoists or other motors, suspension points on flying bars and the centre of a revolve.

The default style is a dot so open the Point Style dialog box by clicking Format ➢ Point Style *Fig 4-19*.

The current Style is highlighted, to select another just click on it.

Next we need to decide how the Point's size is displayed on screen. Try the Relative to Screen size option first (it is the default). Click OK and then draw a Point on your Theatre drawing.

Click Draw ➢ Point

Or Click the Point Icon on the Draw Toolbar

or Type *point* ⏎ at the Command Line

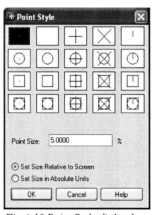

Fig 4-19 Point Style dialog box.

Command: _point

Current point modes:

PDMODE=98   PDSIZE=5.0000

Point icon.

These two values refer to the Style and size that we have set.

Specify a point:

Either pick a point or use a coordinate. As AutoCAD expects you to put in a lot of Points it is now ready for you to give it another coordinate.

Hit Esc

Cancel

You will see that your point is rather large, being

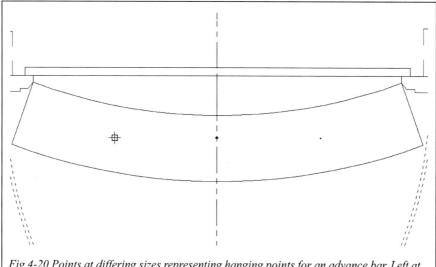

Fig 4-20 Points at differing sizes representing hanging points for an advance bar. Left at 5%, centre at 1%, right at 5mm.

5% of a big drawing area.

Now repeat the exercise, changing the size in the style dialog box to Absolute Units. The Point will change to an object 5mm wide on our stage, probably a bit too small *Fig 4-20.*

I found that 1% was acceptable as it was visible but not too dominating. If you like you can now use your point to mark the centre of the revolve.

Array

We are going to cover over our stage in 8' x 4' ply sheets. To do this in our drawing we will use the array command. This will be considerably easier than the real thing. Obviously we need a new Layer for this so create Layer 2a Stage Floor Colour: Grey, LineType: Continuous, LWT: Default.

Next, we need a sheet of ply, so create a rectangle, 2440 x 1220 with the long side running horizontally.

Now we need to move it to a position stage left, as we want our Array to run only in the positive XY axis to save thinking about minus figures. Move it using the bottom left corner as the base point and place it at 7593, 7853.

Now we are ready to start the Array command so:

Either Click Modify ➢ Array

Click the Array Icon on the Modify Toolbar
or Type `array` ↵ at the Command Line.
The dialog box in *Fig 4-21* will appear

*Array
icon.*

As you can see, there are two alternative methods of array,
Rectangular and Polar. For our
stage covering we need rectangular,
so make sure the correct button is
selected. Next pick on the Select
objects button which will bring you
back into the drawing area, and pick
the rectangle.

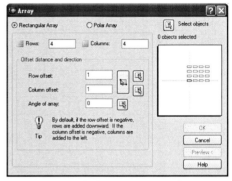

*Fig 4-21 Array dialog box showing the
Rectangular Array Options.*

Now we need to decide how many
Rows and Columns are required to
cover the stage. As the icon shows
Rows run one above (or below)
each other and Columns run across
the screen. Make an estimate of how
many you will need in each then move on to the next section. Before starting
on your offsets though notice that the little preview window is showing you
approximately what your array will look like.

The offsets require a bit of thought here but once you have what is a Row
and what is a Column clear in your mind, this shouldn't present any problems.
In this case, our Row offset is 1220. This will make the next Row butt up to
the top edge of each Row below it. To get the same for our Columns put 2440
in the box.

Alternatively by using the Pick both Offsets Icon with the Osnaps
on you can just pick the diagonally opposite corners of the Rectangle
to define the Array. An advantage of this method is that the order you
pick in defines which way the Array works. If you pick bottom left
then top right, you will create an Array in the positive XY Axis. If you
reverse that you will create one in the negative XY Axis.

*Pick
both
Offsets
icon.*

Exploring this option further, if you pick just the top left and right
corners, again depending on order of pick you will create an Array of
just one row in either the positive or negative axis. It follows that
picking the two endpoints of a vertical will also create an Array, this time a
positive or negative column, again depending on the pick order.

Obviously this works best with rectangles or squares. Try it with Polygons and you'll get some rather strange, if interesting results.

Fig 4-22 Dialog box, which appears once you have created an Array and previewed it.

Once we have defined the Array, we can have a look at it in action by clicking on the Preview button, which takes you back to the drawing with the array in place. Three alternatives are given in the dialog box, *Fig 4-22*. Accept will draw the Array into the model, Modify returns you to the array dialog box to make adjustments, whilst Cancel stops the array command without altering the drawing.

Now we have created the floor covering we should also cover the apron. To do this, just copy the bottom row of sheets and Trim as necessary around the edge of the stage. You will notice that using our first coordinate and arraying from there has left a few odd shapes that would need to be cut. This is particularly true downstage centre and also at the back wall. Feel free to move your array around then so that you get a more efficient use of the timber sheets. To make this easier switch off the Layers that are in the way, such as the Datum and Revolve Layers and make sure Ortho is on so that you can only move up and down or side to side *Fig 4-23*.

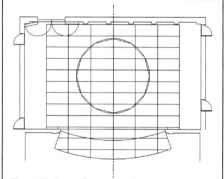

Fig 4-23 Stage floor covering, once trimmed and extended onto the forestage/pit.

Restore any Revolve Layers you just switched off and then switch off the Ply Sheeting Layer.

On the Revolve Layer that the Polygon is on draw a line from a point on the Polygon to the centre of the Circle.

Now restart the Array command and select Polar Array. The

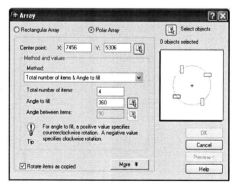

Fig 4-24 Array dialog box showing the Polar Array Options.

Dialogue box will change to look like *Fig 4-24*.

Select the line we just drew, then make the centre of the Circle the centre point of the Array, by picking it using Osnap.

Next, select the method of Arraying. The default should be *Total number of items & Angle to fill*. In the boxes below therefore, the Total number of Items is 12, filling an angle of 360° *Fig 4-25*.

Click on Preview to check what you have created and if it is OK click Accept. Now try drawing the same thing with the other two methods: *Total number of items & Angle between items* and *Angle to fill & Angle between items*. A bit of thought and perhaps maths may be required!

Each method has subtle advantages and disadvantages, depending on what you are trying to do. They can be used to array objects along and arc and the objects can be rotated, so they all face out for instance as they are arrayed.

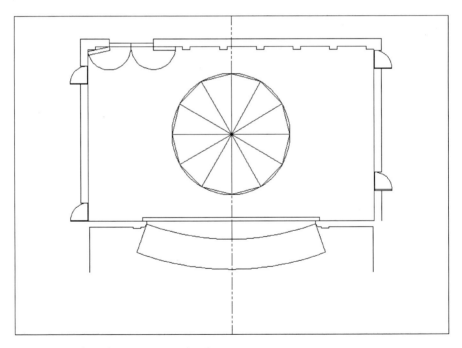

Fig 4-25 Revolve sub structure completed.

Exercise 4

Create flying bars on the ground plan using Polyline and Array. Make the distance between the bars 300mm, with the most downstage bar 400mm from the setting line on the back of the Iron.

Also create the Centre Line and Ends of the Bars as noted in the previous chapter. Use the Layer information from the last chapter to draw your bars on.

Next add the Drencher Pipe. This runs from Stage Right, along the wall and then about 75mm Upstage from the iron, terminating at the Stage Left perch. The Layer information is as follows:

8f Fire – Drencher   Colour: Magenta   LineType: 03W100
LWT: Default

Use Polylines to create the Drencher pipe, which is 50mm wide. Make sure everything ends up on the right Layer!
You should end up with something like *Fig Ex 4 (detail shown).*

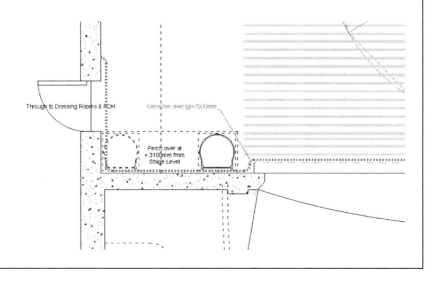

Deforming objects with Grips

Tip!

Let's look at editing Polylines, Polygons, Rectangles and Splines using the Grips and how a designer, when creating a natural shape on a drawing, can use them.

Draw one of each object. The size and components aren't important as we will be changing them. I have created a rather attractive self portrait *Fig B4-1* If you click on any of these you will see they all have Grips either in different places from the same object made from single lines or many more.

Polylines, Rectangles and Polygons keep to straight line transformations, for instance. Polyline arcs, still create Arcs when you move the Grips, just the size (radius) changes.

You can move the Grips about with the mouse or use coordinates. Remember you need to click on the Grip you want to move to make them active —they'll turn red. Here's what I created in a

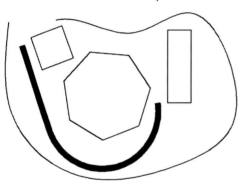

couple of minutes from the base drawing above. *Fig B4-2*

Although AutoCAD does have a sketching facility, deforming a shape with Grips is an easy and elegant solution to creating natural shapes, rather than trying to figure out your coordinates beforehand. This allows a degree of free-hand drawing when trying to create something which is not a geometric object.

5 ADDING INFORMATION TO YOUR DRAWING

Up until this point, we have been looking at the drawing tools we need to create our drawing. However this is not all that is required to convey the required information to our end user, be they the carpenter creating a set or the LX crew rigging the lighting. At some point we are going to have to add some text.

Text

AutoCAD has two types of text, Single Line or Dynamic Text (DText) and Multiline Text (MText). Of these, Single Line text is the one you are likely to use most and is certainly the easiest to use 'on the fly'.

Before we start writing, we should first set up a Text Style or two. The default Text Style for AutoCAD (Standard) uses a rather spidery font. All the fonts in Windows are now free to use in AutoCAD but they must be set up as a Style to make them available.

Text Styles

Open the default Template to practice creating Text. To create a text style pick Format ➢ Text Style.

Or click the Icon on the Style Bar and the Text Style Manager dialog box is shown *Fig 5-1.*

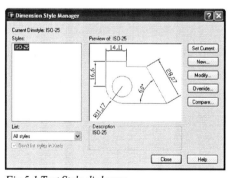

Fig 5.1 Text Style dialogue.

As you can see the default text style is Standard – the font is txt.shx. This is not a True Type font, it is in fact an AutoCAD shape. What your text will look like is shown in the bottom right preview box.

Text Style Manager: icon.

To comply with the CAD Standards we only need two fonts – Major Text and Minor Text. These

Fig 5.2 New Text Style dialogue.

are at set heights to guarantee legibility when plotted at scale. The division between what should be Major and what should be Minor text will vary from theatre to theatre. For instance, in some theatres the height under a fly floor may only need to be added for information. In others this may be a vital statistic for a designer in contemplating scenery storage and movement.

To create these fonts firstly click New in the Style Name area, which brings up a new dialogue box *Fig 5-2* Type Minor Text and then click OK.

Now, using the drop down box in the Font area, pick Arial. The preview box will change to reflect the selection. Now that we have picked a True Type font, the Font Style drop down box is active, we only need regular but have a look at the other options.

Lastly change the height to 100. This will give you a readable height of 4mm when printed at 1:25. See the box below for how the height changes on the printed drawing at various scales. See tip at end of chapter for details.

If you are using text and are unsure of the height you will need, then leave the height at 0. When you are using your text you will be prompted to give a height. However the height specified above conforms to the Standards and guarantees clear printing at 1:25.

Now click Apply and then Close and you have now created a new Text Style.

Your new Style will now appear in the Text drop down on the Style Bar. To make another style active use the drop down to select the Style you want. Obviously it will only show the Styles available *Fig 5-3*.

5.3 Text Styles available from the Style bar.

Create the Major Text Style also at this point. It has the same properties as Minor Text except that its height is 200.

Single Line Text

To start writing pick Draw ➢ Text ➢ Single Line Text

Or Type dtext (for Dynamic text) at the command line

```
Command: dtext
Current text style: "Minor Text" Text height:
```

```
100.0000
Specify start point of text or [Justify/
Style]:
```
Pick a point or enter a coordinate and the text cursor will appear
```
Specify rotation angle of text <0>:
```
Enter the angle you want your text to run at, or accept the default ↵
```
Enter text:
```
Type your text ↵

Your cursor will now be at the beginning of the next line directly below your start point
```
Enter text:
```
either type some more text then ↵ or just
hit ↵ to end the command

If you keep entering text, then hitting ↵ the
cursor will carry on jumping to the next line
Fig 5-4.

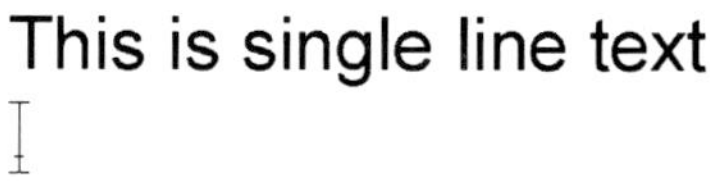

This is single line text

Fig 5.4 Single Line Text creation.

If you are using a font in which no height
is specified then you will get a prompt for a height
```
Specify height <2.5000>:
```
after being asked for the start point and before rotation.

Going back a bit,

If you type J ↵ the command line will change to
```
Enter an option [Align/Fit/Center/Middle/
Right/TL/TC/TR/ML/MC/MR/BL/BC/BR]:
```
Try the various options to see what they do. Fit, for instance, will either squeeze or stretch your text between two points you define. It may look a bit odd as a result! TL, ML, BL etc stand for Top, Middle or Bottom Left of your lettering.

Multiline Text

Although in effect you can use Single Line Text to create more than one line of text, Multiline Text is the 'proper' way to do it.

Either Click Draw ➢ Text ➢ Multiline Text

Click the Mtext Icon on the Draw Toolbar

or Type mtext ↵ at the Command Line.

Mtext
icon.

As soon as you start the command a cross will appear onscreen with *abc* in the current text style attached. *Fig 5-5*

The Command Line will read

```
Command: _mtext Current text
style: "Minor Text" Text height:
100
Specify first corner:
```

Fig 5.5 Multiline Text, defining the area of the text box.

Pick a point or enter a coordinate

```
Specify opposite corner or [Height/Justify/
Line spacing/Rotation/Style/Width]:
```

Either use one of the options or pick a point.

Of the options available both Height and Style can be changed within the command, for the others it's now or never!

Once you have used any options and then picked to set the box size then the Multiline Text Editor appears *Fig 5-6.*

You should be aware from the start that the area where the cursor is and where you will enter text is not the actual size of the box you have just created. As a result your text will

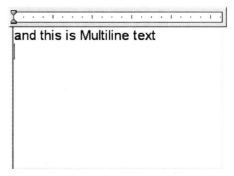

Fig 5.6 Multiline Text Editor, showing the ruler bar.

change to the font size you have defined for it when you have finished writing.

On the top of this box is a ruler showing the current width of the 'page'. Placing your cursor over the end of the ruler and dragging it to the right will pull this out. As you do so a tooltip will tell you the actual size. The lines on the ruler indicate default tabs. To make the whole box bigger, grab a corner with the mouse and pull it out.

Floating above the Editor is the Text Formatting dialog box. This allows you to change some of parameters of the text as you go, meaning that you can have different fonts and heights as well as colours applied as you input text. *Fig 5-7*

When you have finished inputting your deathless prose do not use ⏎ as this

Fig 5.7 Multiline Text Formatting bar.

will just start a new line. Instead use OK in Text Formatting. The text will now take up its true space in your drawing.

Special Symbols

Sometimes we will need to add some symbols into our text. The more obvious ones being the degrees (°) or Diameter (∅).

How you insert these depends on which kind of Text method you are using. In DText you would need to type as follows;

> To add a degree symbol type %%d
> To add a diameter symbol type %%c
> To add a tolerance symbol (±) type %%p

When you hit enter, these will convert into the symbols. In Mtext right clicking in the Text Editor opens a sub menu. Select Symbols then choose from the options.

Editing Text

Editing existing text is very easy; simply double click on your text. Depending on how the text was originally created a dialog box will appear.

In the case of DText it is a simple Edit Text box. Make your changes and click OK *Fig 5-8.*

For MText the Editor and Formatting boxes both appear. Again make any changes then click OK.

Be aware when editing text that if you have used DText to create several lines of text for any editing purposes each line is regarded as an individual object. If you try and pick more than one of them, the Properties dialog box opens. There will be a window under text marked Contents. It will show *VARIES* which is the default if more than one object is picked. If you enter any new text in here then both strings of text will change to your new entry.

Fig 5.8 Single Line Text Editor, used to make alter text. Multiline Text is corrected in the usual editor.

Exercise 5

Add the following notation to your drawing
I will leave you to decide both location and style.

Height Under Fly Floors +6500mm from Stage level

Perch Over @+3100mm from Stage Level

Stage floor @ +900mm from Stalls Level

Orchestra Pit Elevator – Range of Travel +900mm to – 3500mm from Stalls level

I have also added text indicating where all the doors lead. *Fig 5-9*

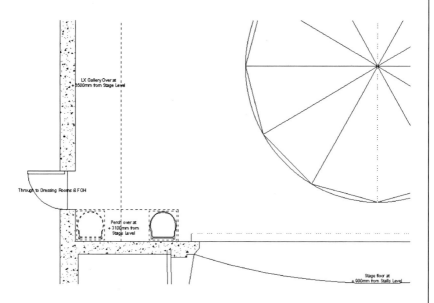

Fig 5.9 Detail of the theatre drawing showing sample text added.

Importing Text

The text editors in AutoCAD are probably not the best place to write great screeds of notes. Instead you can write text in a word processing program such as MS Word or Notepad.

AutoCAD can only import .rtf (Rich Text Files) or .txt (Text) files. There are limitations on text imports however. The file size cannot be more than 32kb which may be restrictive.

Text is imported via the Multiline Text Editor, so open that up, then right click in it to open the sub menu, then click Import Text.

Navigate to the location of your file, then open it by either highlighting it and clicking Open or just double clicking on it. The text will be inserted at your cursor in the Text Editor.

You can now make any adjustments then click OK to add it to the drawing.

Imported text acts the same way as Multiline text but there are differences in the way the two file formats act once imported. .txt files assume the current style and all of its properties. .rtf files on the other hand take on the name only, but stay as they were in the word processing program used to create them.

You will need to do a bit of editing to get them conforming to the rest of the Text Style.

Dimensioning

At some point we will need to add dimensions to a drawing. There is always a degree of uncertainty as to the accuracy of drawings which have been copied. They may have been slightly reduced or enlarged or the paper itself may have changed size slightly. Even with drawings plotted directly from AutoCAD, mistakes can be made.

Having a dimension on it will help, as well as a big line of text saying:
DO NOT SCALE FROM THIS DRAWING

Dimensioning is quite easy in AutoCAD so first we will practice the various methods

Open the Dimensioning drawing, Working Drawings.dwg, *Fig 5-10.* and then create a new Layer – Dimensions. Normally your

Fig 5.10 Working Drawing.dwg.

Dimension layer would be in the Parent group of whatever it is you are measuring, in this case 7 Scenic. The Linetype for dimensions is Continuous with an LWT of 0.35mm.

Before actually dimensioning, there is one adjustment we need to make in the Dimension Style, so that we can read the dimension information as we apply it.

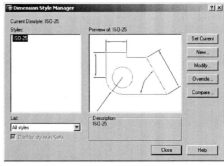

Fig 5.11 The Dimension Style Manager showing the default style.

Pick Format ➢ Dimension Style and the Dialog box appears *Fig 5-11.*

Pick the Modify button and then the Text tab. Alter the text size to 4 *Fig 5-12.*

Now click on the Fit Tab and at the radio button Use overall scale of change it to 25. This will make your dimension text 100mm high (4 x 25).

Click OK then close.

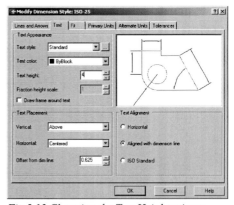

Fig 5.12 Changing the Text Height prior to dimensioning so we can see it.

Linear Dimension

We will always start a dimension command via the Dimension menu, so click

Dimension ➢ Linear. There is a Dimension toolbar, but I want to keep the Drawing area as uncluttered as possible (and I cannot remember all the icons).

We will first measure the top of the left hand flat

```
Command: _dimlinear
Specify first extension line origin or
<select object>:
```
Using the Endpoint Osnap pick either end
```
Specify second extension line origin:
```
Again using Endpoint pick the other end.
```
Specify dimension line location or
[Mtext/Text/Angle/Horizontal/Vertical/
```

```
Rotated]:
  @0,100 ↵
```
I want my Dimension Line to sit 100 above the object I am measuring. You can also pick a point with your mouse
```
Dimension text = 2440
```
The dimension has now been created. Let us zoom in and look at the components of a Dimension *Fig 5-13.*

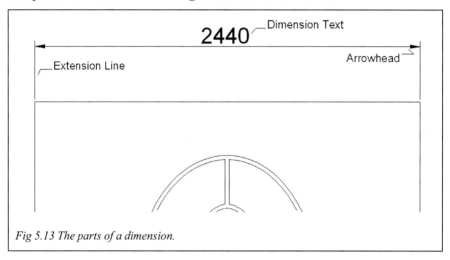

Fig 5.13 The parts of a dimension.

These are the options prior to fixing our dimension line's location.

Mtext	Allows you to enter any text in place of the dimension using the Mtext Editor. You will have to delete the current text first, shown as ◇.
Text	Allows you to change the text at the command line.
Angle	Allows you to alter the angle the text runs at.
Horizontal	Ensures you only measure the horizontal distance.
Vertical	Ensures you only measure the vertical distance. In this case we would create a dimension of 0 as our measurement is horizontal.
Rotated	Alters the angle that the dimension line runs. This will give you a different measurement. See Aligned below.

Aligned

For this measurement, we will use the dado rail running by the stairs on the right hand flat. Again pick the ends using Endpoint and place your line 100 up from the object you are measuring.

```
Command: _dimaligned
Specify first extension line origin or
<select object>:
```

Pick an Endpoint

```
Specify second extension line origin:
```

Pick the other Endpoint

```
Specify dimension line location or
[Mtext/Text/Angle]: @0,100
Dimension text = 3055.21
```

As you have probably guessed this method aligns itself to whatever angle an object is running at. Try dimensioning the same object using Linear. As you can see, there is quite a difference in lengths. *Fig 5-14.*

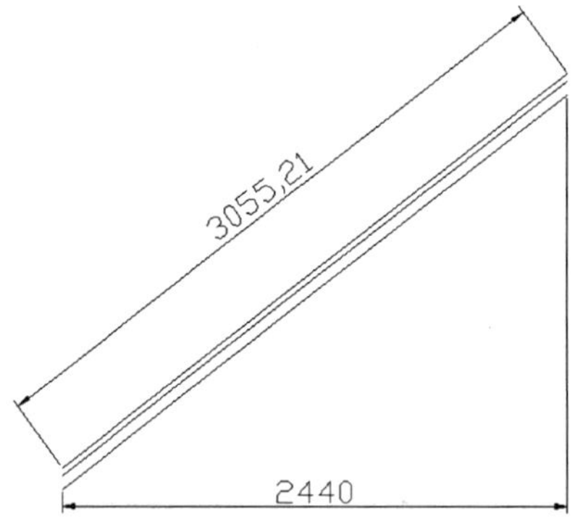

This is a common error made by people drawing plans up: mixing aligned and linear measurements. It is vital, whether drawing in CAD or on paper, that you make clear which measurement is correct. I have seen a lot of time and money wasted by incorrect dimensioning of a simple object due to a lack of understanding of the difference between the two measurements.

Fig 5.14 Aligned Dimension (top) and Linear Dimension (bottom) Although they are both measuring the same object, the values are very different. Confusing these two methods of measuring an object is a common mistake.

Ordinate

This will give you one half of a coordinate to place as a reference on your drawing. Start the command and pick the bottom right corner of the right flat. If you pull your mouse either right or left the dimension that appears is 0 (Y coordinate). Move your mouse up and down and the X coordinate is displayed (7979.28).

This will be useful later, so set it to 0 and leave it.

```
Command: _dimordinate
```

```
Specify feature
location:
```

Pick the Endpoint

```
Specify leader
endpoint or [Xdatum/
Ydatum/Mtext/Text/
Angle]:
```

Pick a point

```
Dimension text = 0
```
See *Fig 5-15.*

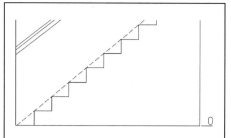

Fig 5.15 Ordinate Dimension in the Y axis added to the corner of the left flat.

Radius

Obviously this will measure Circles or Arcs, so start the command and choose any part of the window in the centre flat.

```
Select arc or circle:
```

The crosshairs become a pick box. I chose the inner arc

```
Dimension text = 690.75
Specify dimension line location or [Mtext/
Text/Angle]:
```

Pick a point.

```
Command:
DIMRADIUS
Select arc or
circle:
```

This time I chose the outer circle

```
Dimension text =
740.75
Specify dimension
line location or
[Mtext/Text/Angle]:
```

The dimension text will be prefixed by R for radius, see *Fig 5-16.*

Notice how the radius lines are slightly different. In one case I place

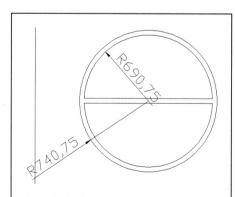

Fig 5.16 Radius measurements showing the different possible placing of the text.

my dimension inside the Arc, the other is outside the circle. In both cases the arrow points to the arc or circle being measured and extends out from the centre of that object.

Diameter

Diameter works in just the same way as Radius. This time there are two arrows defining the measurement, even in the case of an arc if you move your mouse to the outside of the arc.

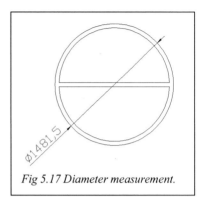

Fig 5.17 Diameter measurement.

```
Command: _dimdiameter
Select arc or circle:
Dimension text = 1381.5
Specify dimension line
location or [Mtext/Text/
Angle]:
```

Pick a point

The dimension text is prefixed by the diameter symbol ∅ *Fig 5-17*.

Angular

Use the Elliptical window on which to practice this command. You may have noticed that you cannot get Radius or Diameters for this object as it is a trimmed Ellipse. What look like arcs do not count for the dimensioning tools.

```
Command: _dimangular
Select arc, circle, line, or <specify
vertex>:
```

Select a line on the window frame

```
Select second line:
```

Select the next line around

```
Specify dimension arc line location or
[Mtext/Text/Angle]:
```

Pick a point

```
Dimension text = 45
```

Fig 5-18 is what I created. If you move your mouse around when asked to pick a point you will see other angles being formed all taken from the two points you have picked.

Now try getting an angular dimension from the outer part of the circular window.

```
Command: _dimangular
Select arc, circle,
line, or <specify
vertex>:
```

Pick a point on the circle.

```
Specify second angle
endpoint:
```

A line is formed from the first point back to the centre point of the circle. As you move your mouse it swings with you. Click on another part of the circle.

```
Specify dimension arc
line location or [Mtext/
Text/Angle]:
```

Now move your mouse and an angular dimension is shown between the two points.

Move the mouse in the opposite direction and a larger angle is formed. Choose which one you want to measure

```
Dimension text = 290
```

or 70 in this case *Fig 5-19.*

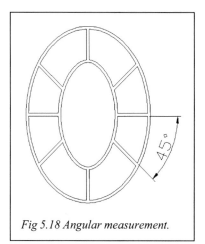

Fig 5.18 Angular measurement.

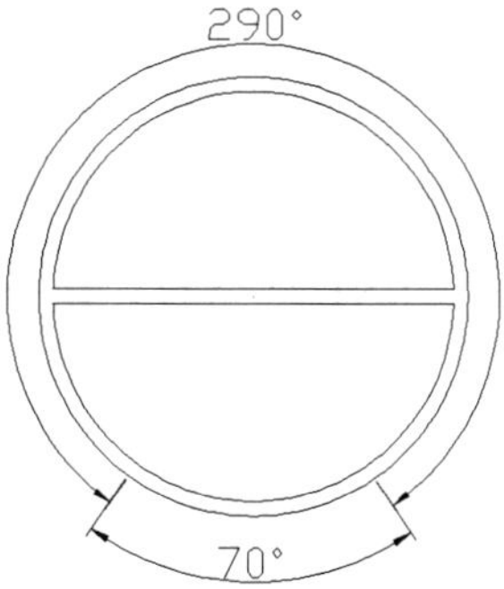

Fig 5.19 Angular measurement showing the two different possible values whilst measuring on a circle.

Baseline

Baseline adds an incremental dimension from a given point or dimension. It therefore always needs an original dimension to work from.

Firstly we will use it with the Ordinate dimension we created earlier. Start the command. Use the drawing in *Fig 5-20* to see which parts of the flat I picked.

```
Command: _dimbaseline
Select base dimension:
```

Pick the 0 Ordinate dimension

```
Specify feature location or [Undo/Select]
<Select>:
Dimension text = 1850.52
Specify feature location or [Undo/Select]
<Select>:
Dimension text = 2746.19
Specify feature location or [Undo/Select]
<Select>:
Dimension text = 3063.75
Specify feature location or [Undo/Select]
<Select>:
Dimension text = 3363.75
Specify feature location or [Undo/Select]
<Select>:
Dimension text = 4291.44
Specify feature location
or [Undo/Select]
<Select>:
Dimension text = 6100
Specify feature location
or [Undo/Select]
<Select>: ↵
```

As you can see you now have a series of measurements showing the height above zero of the various parts of the flat. If you use an Ordinate dimension but have for some reason changed the text, the Baseline dimension will still read the actual Ordinate's true location. So if you place an Ordinate at 100mm but change the text to 0, the Baselines will still measure from the 100mm mark.

Now let us use Baseline with a Linear Dimension. Create a Linear dimension on the left hand side of the left flat, from the

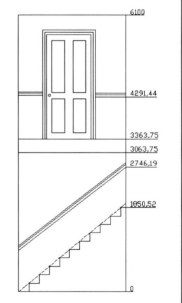

Fig 5.20 Baseline dimension created using our Ordinate dimension.

base to the dado rail. Once you have done that start the Baseline command. It will automatically start from the dimension you have just created.

```
Command:
Command: _dimbaseline
Specify a second extension line origin or
[Undo/Select] <Select>:
Dimension text = 1037.68
Specify a second extension line origin or
[Undo/Select] <Select>:
Dimension text = 3050
Specify a second extension line origin or
[Undo/Select] <Select>:
Dimension text = 3200
Specify a second extension line origin or
[Undo/Select] <Select>:
Dimension text = 6100
Specify a second
extension line origin or
[Undo/Select] <Select>:
```

See *Fig 5-21*.

If you are returning to an old dimension you must use Select at the command line to pick the dimension from which you wish to create the baseline. Once you have picked the dimension, then the command starts creating the other dimension lines as above. As you can see, the offset of each dimension is not sufficient to read it clearly. See the Tips at the end of this chapter for a cure.

Continue

Continue will create dimensions between points using the second extension line as a starting point for the first dimension. In other words, it acts like Baseline does with

Fig 5.21 Baseline dimension created from a Linear dimension.

an Ordinate dimension but showing distances. However, if you use it with an Ordinate dimension, it works just like Baseline does.

Before starting this command undo or erase your Baseline dims. We will use the same Linear dimension as a starting point.

```
Command: _dimcontinue
Select continued dimension:
```

Pick the Linear Dimension

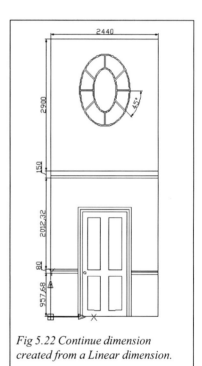

```
Specify a second
extension line origin or
[Undo/Select] <Select>:
Dimension text = 80
Specify a second
extension line origin or
[Undo/Select] <Select>:
Dimension text = 2012.32
Specify a second
extension line origin or
[Undo/Select] <Select>:
Dimension text = 150
Specify a second
extension line origin or
[Undo/Select] <Select>:
Dimension text = 2900
Specify a second
extension line origin or
[Undo/Select] <Select>:
```

See *Fig 5-22.*

Fig 5.22 Continue dimension created from a Linear dimension.

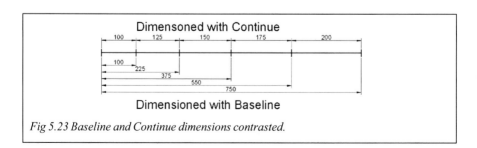

Dimensoned with Continue

Dimensioned with Baseline

Fig 5.23 Baseline and Continue dimensions contrasted.

Fig 5-23 summarises the differences and similarities between Baseline and Continuous dimensions.

Leader

A leader is simply a way of pointing at something with text attached to the end of your arrow. The text can be anything and can be entered at the command line or with MTEXT. Start the Leader command:

```
Command: _qleader
Specify first leader point, or [Settings]
<Settings>:
```

This is the pointing end. Pick somewhere near or on the object that the Leader refers to.

```
Specify next point:
```

Pick a point

```
Specify next point:
```

Pick a point

```
Specify text width <0>:
```

Enter first line of annotation text <Mtext>: Practical Sash Window ⏎
Enter next line of annotation text: ⏎ see *Fig 5-24.*

Now you may have notice we needed to pick a couple of points for our leader to run through. This can be a bit irritating, so start Leader again and enter *S* to get to the Leader Settings dialog box *Fig 5-25.*

Click on the Leader Line & Arrow tab and in the bottom left make the maximum number of points 2. You now will only have to click to define where the arrow goes and the end of the line.

You can also set your Leader line as a Spline rather than a straight line. Although

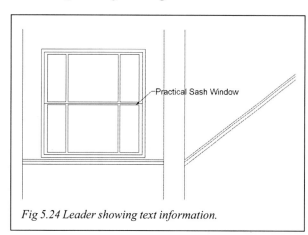

Fig 5.24 Leader showing text information.

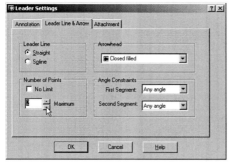

Fig 5.25 Leader Settings dialogue.

this is not part of the Standard it could be used to add additional notes of changes to a drawing etc.

Dimension Styles

We have been using the dimension tools with mainly the default settings. Although this will be fine for most things, on a more complex drawing, particularly ones showing both the structure of the theatre as well as the show and their relationships the Standards have different styles for certain measurements.

We can set up a range of dimension styles to use for particular jobs on a drawing. All of these will be easily accessible via the Style Bar, so we can use them as and when required.

Again, the ABTT CAD Standards will define our styles.

We need to create two styles for the simple reason that within the standards there are two types of dimension: those that refer to the structure of the venue called Surveyed Reference Dimensions and those that refer to objects within the building such as scenery, technical equipment etc; the Object Size Dimensions.

Click Format ➤ Dimension Style

Or pick the icon on the Style Bar to open the Dimension Style Manager *Fig 5-26.*

Dimension Style Manager icon.

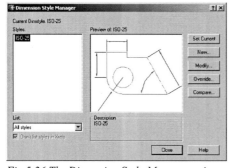

Fig 5.26 The Dimension Style Manager prior to creating a new Style.

As you can see, there is already a dimension style ISO25. This is because we are in an ISO template. Click New to open the next dialog box *Fig 5-27.*

The New Style Name is ABTT Surveyed Reference. We are basing it on the ISO25 style (there isn't any choice!), which means we use that style as a starting point and customise it. We are going to use this as a Parent Style, so now just click Continue. A new dialog box opens on the Lines and Arrows tab. It is in these tabs we modify styles.

Change the current settings as follows (I will only show the changes):

Lines and Arrows Tab

`Baseline Spacing 6`

This is the amount the dimension lines offset each other when using Baseline. Our dimension text will be 100 high, so this will create a space once we have set the overall scale. *Fig 5-28*.

Now move to the Text tab

```
Text Height 4
Text Placement;
Horizontal At Ext
Line 1
```

This part of the Standard requires the dimension text to be placed by a dimension arrow. The arrows are at the top of each extension line. You will define which line is Extension Line1 depending on the order you picked when creating the dimension. This can be different each time so it is important you are consistent in your dimensioning.

Note in this tab that you can also set a text style. As we have set up our Standard text style, we should use this one, but any text style that has been created is accessible via the drop down box. Using a Text Style will, however, override any

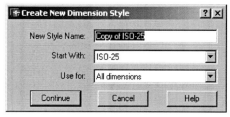

Fig 5.27 Create New Dimension Style dialogue.

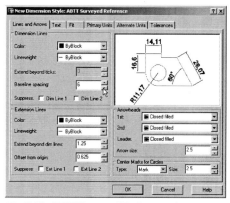

Fig 5.28 ABTT Surveyed Reference dimension style; Lines and arrows tab.

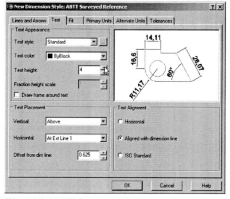

Fig 5.29 ABTT Surveyed Reference dimension style; Text tab.

settings for Text Size or Fit in the Dimension Style *Fig 5-29.*

On the Fit tab change this

```
Scale for Dimension
Features; Use overall
scale of 25.
```

With our earlier changes this makes our text 100 high and our Baseline offsets 150, making them readable. *Fig 5-30*

Primary Units tab:

```
Linear Dimensions;

Precision    0.0

Decimal Separator
'.' (Period)
```

See *Fig 5-31.*

The Alternate Units tab would allow you to add feet and inches in brackets after your metric measurements. Tolerances would add the ± symbol together with the degree of accuracy set.

We do not require either of these, so click OK. You are returned to the first dialog box. Your new style is shown and in the Preview box you will see all of the changes you have made. *Fig 5-32*

With the new style highlighted, once again click New and from the bottom box select Linear dimensions. When you look at the tabs, the Parent style has been copied across. Note how in the Primary Units tab, the Angular Dimension area is greyed out, because of our selection of this style as Linear dimensions only. The only change you

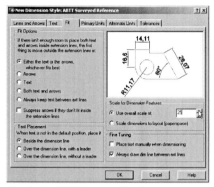

Fig 5.30 ABTT Surveyed Reference dimension style; Fit tab.

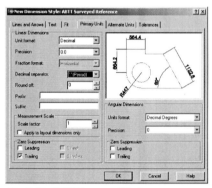

Fig 5.31 ABTT Surveyed Reference dimension style; Primary Units tab.

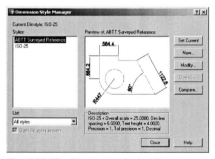

Fig 5.32 The Dimension Style Manager with the new Style being previewed.

would need to make is to add a Suffix of mm in the Primary Units tab.

Now repeat creating a child Dimension Style so that the mm suffix appears on all the other measurements you may need, that is, Radius, Diameter and Ordinate. Once these are set up, the correct suffix will be automatically added to your dimensions.

The Leader setting, which is a closed, filled Arrowhead is used in the Standard to show a Leader to the Outline of an object. We will set up the Leader to a Surface setting when we create the Object Size Dim Style. Note that in the Angular measurements you cannot add a suffix. If we had set the Parent Style with the mm suffix added to our dimensions it would also add it to the angular measurement, which is nonsense, unless °mm means something to you.

When you have set up your styles, close the box and then select ABTT Surveyed Reference from the style bar. As you use each type of dimension, then the style will apply the settings you have created.

By creating a Parent and Child dimension style we have saved ourselves from constantly changing styles or editing dimension text on the fly.

Exercise 6

Create the following Dimension Style, which is based on the ABTT Surveyed Reference

Dimension Style Title   ABTT Object Size

Here are the only changes required:

Lines and arrows Tab

1st and 2nd Arrowheads   Architectural Ticks

Leader   Dot

Text Tab

Text Placement; Horizontal Centered

You will also need to create a Linear, Radial, Diameter and Ordinate Dimension Child Styles to add mm to your measurements.

An object dimensioned with both styles is shown below so you can see the differences.

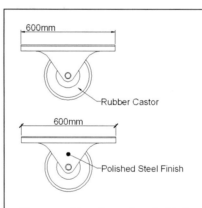

The same object dimensioned with the two styles. The Top is the ABTT Surveyed Reference Style, the bottom the ABTT Object Size Style. Obviously you would not dimension the same object with the two styles, this is purely for comparison

Associative Dimensions

Dimensions are, by default associative in AutoCAD. This means that once a dimension is created it is associated with the object it has measured. Should there be changes to that object then the dimension will be updated automatically. Let us change a couple of lines in the drawing and watch the dimensions update themselves. You can use any method to change things. In this case I will use Grips.

As I make the Grip hot, I can move it where I will and as I release it, the dimension will stretch out to the new endpoint and update the value.

Let us look at a couple of other modifying methods that you may use.

Scale

We will scale the circular window, which we have previously added both radii and diameters to

Scale asks for a value and much the same as LTS, 1 is the default; more than one is bigger, less than one smaller.

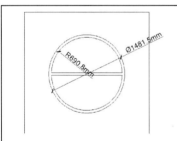

Fig 5.33a The round window and dimensions prior to Scaling.

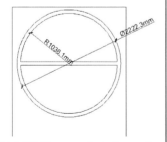

Fig 5.33b The round window and dimensions after Scaling.

Either Click Modify ➢ Scale

Click the Scale Icon on the Modify Toolbar

or Type `scale` ↵ at the Command Line

Scale Icon.

`Command: _scale`

`Select objects: Specify opposite corner: 6 found`

I used a crossing window to pick up the whole window.

`Select objects ↵`

`Specify base point:`

Use the Center Osnap

`Specify scale factor or [Reference]: 1.5`

The window is now half as big again and any dimensions have also updated themselves. Figs *5-33a* & *5-33b*.

Stretch

Stretch works by using a crossing window to select the objects. Tt will only work with a crossing window (or polygon) so in some instances you will need to be careful about your selection.

The left hand flat needs to be wider so we will stretch that by another half a sheet (1220mm) to the left.

Either Click Modify ➤ Stretch

Click the Stretch Icon on the Modify Toolbar

or Type stretch ↵ at the Command Line

Stretch Icon.

```
Command: _stretch
```

Select objects to stretch by crossing-window or crossing-polygon...

```
Select objects: Specify opposite corner: 9
found
```

Create your window across the left hand side of the flat. Make sure you pick up the picture and dado rails but avoid the door.

```
Select objects: ↵
Specify base point or displacement:
```

Pick any point on the left edge of the flat (use an Osnap).

```
Specify second point of displacement or <use
first point as displacement>: @-1220,0
```

The flat is now that bit bigger and the dimension has updated itself. *Figs 5-34a & 5-34b.*

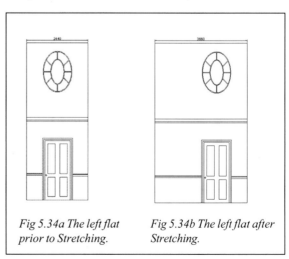

Fig 5.34a The left flat prior to Stretching.

Fig 5.34b The left flat after Stretching.

Scales within AutoCAD

As we have seen earlier with Linetype Scale there are two parts to an object's scale within AutoCAD, that of the individual object and that of the overall style. This kind of scale should not be confused with scale for printing, although your ultimate output scale is a factor in deciding these sizes.

Scaling Text

There is a simple bit of maths required to set up a text scale, but don't panic, it is very simple, no calculator required.

Firstly, to create Major Text, which is 8mm high when plotted, we multiply our target height by the scale we are using;

8 x 25 = 200

We should therefore make our text 200 high on our drawing.

To find out how big our text will be when plotted, this time using a height of 100 (Minor Text), we do the reverse calculation

100 ÷ 25 = 4

Our text will be 4mm high when plotted at 1:25. This calculation is considerably more complicated using imperial measurements!

Font Heights at Scale

Font height in drawing	Plotted scale	Font height when plotted
100 (Minor Text Style)	1:25	4mm
	1:50	2mm
	1:75	1.33mm
	1:100	1mm
200 (Major Text Style)	1:25	8mm
	1:50	4mm
	1:75	2.66mm
	1:100	2mm

Scaling Dimensions

The same kind of maths applies to Dimension Scales, the difference being that the overall scale applies to all the elements of the Style, including Arrowheads, as well as the text itself.

Because of this, it is not unusual to have the individual parts of a dimension set to particular sizes, whilst using an overall scale to keep them relative to each other.

In the case of the Standards we have set the dimension text at 100 by making the text height 4 and using an overall scale of 25 (4 x 25 = 100)

To keep the dimension text tidy when using the Baseline function we set a scale of 6. This will mean each baseline jumps 150 (6 x 25 = 150), with our dimension text set at 100, this creates a nice space around each dimension *Fig B5-1*

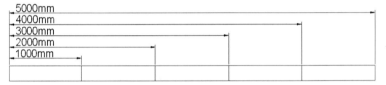

Fig B5-1 Baseline dimensions clearly spaced so that the text is legible.

The arrowheads were not altered and have a default height of 2.5 meaning that after scaling by 25, they are actually 62.5 high on the drawing. These parameters are not set in the Standards, so you can change them as you see fit. Remember that you are conveying vital dimensional information so keep it as clear as possible.

Of course both of these elements will revert back to their non-scaled heights on plotting at 1:25; that is text 4mm high, arrowheads 2.5mm high.

Yo will need to recalculate this for each scale. Once you have done that these styles can be part of your templates so you don't have to recreate them.

Do not start making them in each template though. As we shall see in Chapter 6 there is a way of creating most things once then placing them into each of your templates.

When you are creating scales etc for your template it is worth also actually drawing a Scale bar, such as *Fig B5-2*, on the plan. This gives everyone a reference from which to measure. Sometimes drawings are not plotted or copied correctly and if you have your suspicions, a check with a scale rule against the scale bar will quickly tell you if they are justified or not.

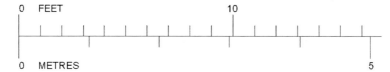

Fig B5-2 Scale Bar.

6 DRAWINGS WITHIN DRAWINGS

Earlier in the book, we noted that in using AutoCAD or indeed any CAD system you should never draw the same thing twice. In this chapter, we will explore the ways of sharing common drawings and the constituent parts of drawings.

Why would we want to include one drawing into another? It is inevitable that in creating a production, often for financial reasons you will include items that already exist in the theatre's stock. This may include such items as rostra, treads, even flattage, doors etc. In the LX department, they will presumably hold a stock of lanterns, which would be tedious to recreate each time.

Once you have drawn an object it can be inserted into another drawing, such as your groundplan template, with ease. Additionally, information can be added to these drawings that can then be extracted to a spreadsheet program allowing kit lists, bills for equipment hires, hanging plots, etc to be generated.

There are two main ways to create and use such drawings. It is important that it is understood how each can be used and how, combined, they form a powerful method of keeping production drawings up to date and accurate.

Blocks

Blocks are drawings, which can contain information that can be inserted into another drawing. Blocks can be any size of drawing or any object. This can range from common elements held in stock, from nuts and bolts through to a complete set inserted into several theatres' groundplans as part of planning a tour.

Traditionally there were two kinds of Block; those that were created as part of a drawing and could be inserted only into that drawing (Blocks) and those that were drawings which could be added to any other drawing (Wblocks). Nowadays we can save any drawing and insert it into another drawing, so we do not need to create Wblocks as special entities.

As well as the actual models contained within a drawing file, there are also other useful things that we may want to reuse. The various Styles we have created do not need to be recreated each time. Although it is best to make a template with everything included it may be that you only need one particular

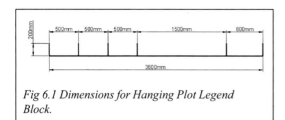

Fig 6.1 Dimensions for Hanging Plot Legend Block.

part of the drawing such as a Dimension Style. As we shall see later this is now easily done and saves a lot of repetition in creating drawings.

We will create a Block to use on our Theatre Groundplan. This block is not an actual object we would use every day but a Hanging Plot Legend. Using the information in it we will be able to create a Hanging Plot in a spreadsheet that will contain the information required to hang an incoming show.

Open the Theatre Drawing and set Layer 4a current. See the Chapter tips for more information on Layers, and Blocks.

Draw a line from the Stage Left end of the most downstage bar out to the border. Next, in the same area draw what is shown in *Fig 6.1*. Now we will add information (known as attributes) to this, or rather we will add the places – called Tags – where the information will go.

Any kind of information can be added as an Attribute. For instance a piece of Steeldeck in a company's hire stock could have the following: Weight, Height of any Legs and the hire cost.

How or if these are displayed is set in the Define attributes dialogue box. The options are:

Invisible	The attribute will not be displayed. In our Steeldeck example the hire cost may be set as invisible.
Constant	The attribute value is entered in this dialogue box. The weight of the Steeldeck would be a constant attribute.
Verify	This will require a value to be entered when the block is inserted into the drawing, such as the leg height on the Steeldeck.
Preset	If you set a Preset value then the attribute will revert to this upon insertion.

A combination of these settings can be used, for instance as hire prices may vary then both Invisible and Verify could be used.

Fig 6.2 Attribute Definition dialogue.

BAR#				

Fig 6.3 Hanging Plot Block with Bar Attribute added.

BAR#	DIST	SWL	ITEM	WEIGHT

Fig 6.4 Completed Hanging Plot Block.

Open the Attribute Definition dialogue box by clicking Draw ➢ Block ➢ Define Attributes *Fig 6.2*. Starting at the left of the dialogue tick the Verify box. This means that when you insert the Block it will ask you for an input. In the Tag box type Bar#. In the Prompt box type Bar Number? Next, change the Text Style to Minor Text and lastly use the Pick Point button to place the text. Once you have picked you are returned to the dialogue box. Click OK and your handiwork is revealed *Fig 6.3*. What is shown at the moment is the Tag indicating where the Attribute is and allowing you to identify it. Only when the block is inserted and you have responded to the prompt with a value, will you see the actual Attribute.

Input the remaining Attributes as shown in *Fig 6.4* The Safe Working Load Attribute can be set as a Constant of 400kg

Now we are ready to convert the drawing into a Block.

Fig 6.5 Block Definition dialogue.

Either Click Draw➢Block➢Make

Or the Make Block Icon to open the Block Definition window *Fig 6.5*.

Make Block icon.

In the Name enter Hanging Plot. When you enter this a dialogue will pop up asking you if you want to select the objects to make up the block. At this point we need to be careful as the order in which we select the Attributes determines the order they appear in at the prompt and other dialogues.

Pick the lines first then the Attributes in this order: Bar Number; Distance from The Setting Line; Safe Working Load; Item to be flown; Weight of the Item

Check the Delete button in this area. We don't really need the original, just the block.

Next, use the Pick Point button to select the corner to the left of the Bar# tag. When we insert the Block this point will appear at the crosshairs or if you specify a coordinate this is the point that will be placed there. The Base point for each Block will be different according to its use. For Steeldeck you may use a corner of the unit, a Lantern, the hook clamp. For an entire set it may be the point that the Setting and Centre Lines cross. Even if you do not get the right base point, once a Block is inserted it can be moved like any other object. Blocks are more like Polylines in this respect. Any block, no matter how many constituent parts, will move as one object.

When everything is done click OK. The Hanging plot is now available to use in the drawing.

Inserting Blocks

We can now insert the Hanging Plot onto the drawing.

Either Click Insert ➤ Block

Or pick the Insert Block icon

Insert Block icon.

The Insert window opens, showing our Block in the top box *Fig 6.6.* As you can see we can specify position, scale and rotation of the object. As the Specify onscreen check is selected click OK and the Hanging Plot appears with its base point at the crosshairs. Place it on the line from the first bar we drew earlier, making sure it is inside the inner border.

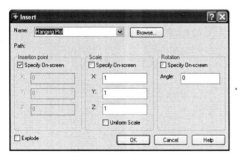
Fig 6.6 Insert Block dialogue.

At the command line the prompts for the Attributes will appear. Fill in those that you can as follows:

Bar Number? CW1

Distance from SL(mm) 410

All the Attributes will be repeated at the command line, with your values in parentheses, for

CW 1 | 410 | 400Kg

Fig 6.7 Hanging Plot block after insertion and Attribute values are added.

verification. Hit ↵ to accept them, or edit them if they are wrong. When you hit enter the last time the block appears together with the values you have entered. *Fig 6-7.*

You can now add a Hanging Plot block for each bar using Array. The bars are at 300 centres and there are 36 of them. Once you have done that, you will need to renumber them and amend the distances using an Attribute Editor.

Fig 6.8 Edit Attribute dialogue.

There are two types of Attribute Editor and both work in essentially the same way.

Typing `attedit` at the Command Line produces `Select block reference:` Pick a block to open the Edit Attributes dialogue. Make your changes and click OK, *Fig 6.8.*

Double clicking on the Block will open the Enhanced Attribute Editor *Fig 6.9.* As well as being able to change the Attribute values you can also amend the appearance of the text and Layer information for each attribute.

Once you have amended all your blocks, at the top of your Hanging Plot add an extra block. Don't bother putting any Attribute information in. Instead, pick on the Explode Icon on the Modify tool bar and pick this new block. Exploding a block returns it to its original parts. You will see the tags now so it is a useful reminder of what each entry means.

Explode icon.

The block we have just created is currently available only to our Theatre drawing. It is a standard block that you would probably want to use in other drawings. How would we get around this problem?

The obvious answer would have been to draw the block as a new drawing. Once it is saved it can then be placed into any other drawing. You would need to redefine the Base point, otherwise 0,0,0 will be used, but this is easily done by using Draw➤Blocks➤Base and then using

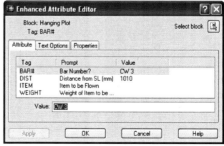

Fig 6.9 Enhanced Attribute Editor.

an Osnap to pick your new insert point. By then saving the drawing, when you next insert it, this is the point that appears at the crosshairs.

You can do this with any existing drawing or any new ones you create that would be useful components in future drawings

The drawing would be inserted just the same as a block via Insert ➤ Block except that you would need to use the Browse button to go to where you saved the drawing. Once you have inserted a drawing it will always be available without the need to browse for it; just use the drop down box in the Insert window.

Exercise 6

Create a Title Block for your theatre. *Fig 6.10* is a typical style.

Add Attributes as necessary, together with prompts etc. The Attributes should be in the Minor Text Style. When it is done, make it a block and insert it in the bottom right corner of the drawing.

Theatre Name	Contact Information
VENUE	
PRODUCTION	
DIRECTOR	
SET DESIGN	
LX DESIGN	
TITLE	
DRWG NO	DRAWN BY
SCALE	DATE
REVISIONS	

Fig 6.10 Sample Title Block.

Attribute Extraction

Now that we have our Hanging Plot Legend, we are going to produce a spreadsheet with any information on it, which can then be distributed.

The first thing we need to do therefore is add some information to the Legend. Add in a few LX bars, some borders and perhaps a cyc. Do not exceed the SWL!

Fig 6.11 Attribute Extraction Dialogue – Select Drawing.

Now click Tools ➤ Attribute Extraction to open the Wizard *Fig 6.11*.

The first screen defines what we are picking. As these are our only blocks currently we can leave the default selection as is. If you have only a few of many blocks you wish to extract information from you can use the Select Objects option. Click Next

Fig 6.12 Attribute Extraction Dialogue – Settings.

Fig 6.12 The next window gives us options over other drawings within our current one. X refs are discussed in Chapter 7, whilst Nested Blocks are in the Tips at the end of the chapter. Click Next.

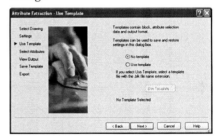

Fig 6.13 Attribute Extraction Dialogue – Use Template.

Fig 6.13 As this is our first Extraction there is no template. Once we have made our choices in this wizard though we can save them as a template to use later on. Click Next.

Fig 6.14 Now we select the Attributes we wish to extract. As you can see the left pane shows the block available and the right what we can extract. Note that there is a lot more information available apart from our definitions.

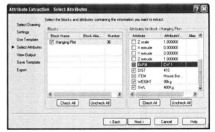

Fig 6.14 Attribute Extraction Dialogue – Select Attributes.

Fig 6.15 Attribute Extraction Dialogue —
View Output.

Fig 6.16 Attribute Extraction Dialogue —
Save Template.

Make sure just our relevant attributes are checked then Click Next.

Fig 6.15 You can now make a choice as to the Appearance of your attributes in the spreadsheet. In this case, the default with columns of information running to the right suits us best. Click Next.

Fig 6.16 This window is where you would save your template, for now click next.

Fig 6.17 Attribute Extraction Dialogue –
Export.

Fig 6.17 You now name your Spreadsheet file and decide your format. In my case it is Microsoft Excel® (.xls).

Save the file and then open it up in your Spreadsheet program. You may need to format it slightly but you now have a Hanging Plot ready for distribution direct from your working drawing. *Fig 6.18.*

Fig 6.18 Our information as it appears in
Microsoft Excel®.

DesignCenter

The DesignCenter allows you to gain access not only to Drawings and Blocks but other parts of a drawing, such as LineTypes, Text Styles etc.

Open a new drawing and then open the DesignCenter.

Either Click Tools ➤ DesignCenter
or Click the Icon on the Standard Toolbar
or Type *adcenter* ↵ at the Command line.
Or use Ctrl + 2. *Fig 6.19.*

*AutoCAD
Design
Center
icon.*

Fig 6.19 AutoCAD DesignCenter.

There are several sample drawings included when you install AutoCAD and we will use one of these to show how the DesignCenter works. Using the left pane, ensuring the tab is set to Folders, Navigate to AutoCAD2004\Sample\DesignCenter

If you now click on the DesignCenter folder the tree will open below it to show all the drawings in the folder. At the same time in the top right pane, small icons will appear representing each drawing. Now that these are in the right pane, they can be dragged and dropped into your current drawing. This applies to any drawing that you have *Fig 6.20.*

*Fig 6.20 AutoCAD DesignCenter showing a
folder and the drawings within it as icons in the
right pane.*

When you drag the drawings icon into the Drawing Area the Command Line will read:

```
Command: _-INSERT Enter block name or [?]:
block box.dwg
Specify insertion point or [Scale/X/Y/Z/
Rotate/PScale/PX/PY/PZ/PRotate]:
```

Click a point

```
Enter X scale factor, specify opposite
corner, or [Corner/XYZ] <1>: ↵
Enter Y scale factor <use X scale factor>: ↵
Specify rotation angle <0>: ↵
```

These command line entries replicate the information in the Insert dialogue.

Click on one of the + next to one of the drawings in the folder *Fig 6.21.* The tree expands again to show all the objects contained in the drawing.

Click on Blocks and in the top right pane all of the blocks in the drawing are shown as icons. *Fig 6.22* Click on one of the block icons and a more detailed icon appears in the pane below with any description below that.

Fig 6.21 AutoCAD DesignCenter showing the parts of a drawing available for use in other drawings.

The drawings contained in the DesignCenter folder are parts libraries. This is very useful in a theatre situation where stock is frequently re-used.

All that is required is to draw up your stock of units such as treads, as blocks within a drawing entitled Stock Treads, for instance. Opening this drawing loads all the treads ready for use.

Alternatively, you could create all your treads as separate drawings in one Stock Treads folder. Then when required, using DesignCenter, open the folder and the drawings will appear in the right pane ready for dragging and dropping.

In many ways it depends on how you want to organise your files and folders.

You can also see from this that other parts of a drawing can be placed within another. As I mentioned in the previous chapter, repeating the creation of Dimension or Text styles on each new drawing is pointless, if you are not or have forgotten to use a template then all these Styles, Layers, LineTypes etc can be dragged and dropped via the DesignCenter into another drawing.

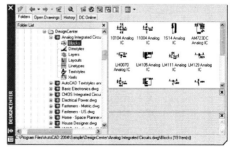

Fig 6.22 AutoCAD DesignCenter showing the blocks within a Library drawing. These can now be drag and dropped into other drawings.

Exercise 7

Using the DesignCenter, insert the seating as shown in *Fig 6.23* There are two blocks in the Seating Library.dwg which have their own Layers, already set up for you

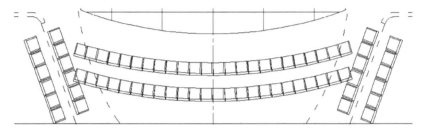

Fig 6.23 The theatre with the two seating Blocks added.

The front row is 1100 from the front of the stage to allow a clear gangway

The circle seating will need to be rotated. Other editing may also be required to get the drawing looking right.

Once the seats are located correctly, on appropriate layers add the sightlines from the extreme ends of each row.

Tool Palettes

The Tool Palettes window, as I mentioned in Chapter 1, holds groups of Blocks or Hatches. We will talk about Hatches later in this chapter. For now, we will look at customising the Tool Palette to create two Palettes of Lanterns. Open the Tool Palette window.

Either Click Tools ➤ Tool Palettes Window

or Click the Tool Palettes icon on the Standard Toolbar

or Type toolpalettes ↵ at the Command line.

Or use Ctrl + 3

Tool Palettes icon.

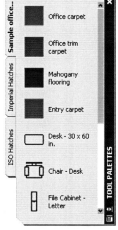

The default window appears, *Fig 6.24.* There are two tabs (actually the Palettes) of Hatches and one with both blocks and hatches. To insert any of them just drag and drop them into the drawing area. As I said earlier, it is not intended that these Palettes are used as supplied but customised by the user.

We will create a Tool Palettes window for an LX department. Open the Lanterns folder in DesignCenter and have a look at what we have in there. You should have a group of 15 lanterns in the folder, all of which will display their icons in the right

Fig 6.24 The default Tool Palette Window.

pane when you click on the folder.

Now right click on the Tool Palettes window and on the pop up menu select New Tool Palette *Fig 6.25.* Name it FOH Rig. Next, create a second palette named General Rig. You can delete the other tabs by clicking on them to make them active, then right clicking and selecting Delete Tool palette. A warning box will appear but click OK and the Tool Palette is gone *Fig 6.26.*

The next thing to do is add our

Fig 6.25 The first custom Tool Palette – FoH Rig showing the icons of the blocks.

Fig 6.26 AutoCAD alert prior to deleting a Tool Palette.

Lanterns into the appropriate tab again. This is done by dragging and dropping. I have put the Narrow profiles into the FOH Palettes and everything else into the General Tab. *Fig 6.27*

The Tool Palette window remains the same no matter which drawing is open so you will wish to create individual Tool Palettes for various departments' PCs within the theatre..

Now we have our Tool Palettes set up we can just drag and drop into our drawing. Grab any one of the Lanterns and drop it into the drawing area.

There are two useful editing commands that we can use with Blocks and many other objects in drawing up scenery or lighting or in fact any other items that make up part of a performance.

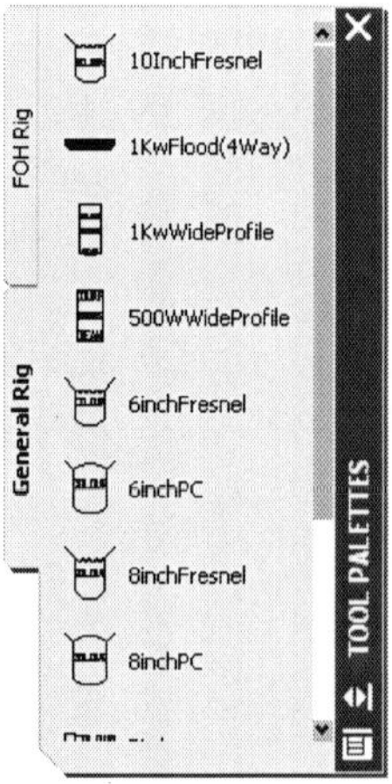

Fig 6.27 The second Tool Palette – General Rig. Again, the blocks can be drag and dropped into the drawing.

Break

Break, as the name suggests, allows us to break an object in a variety of ways. In this case when I insert a Lantern onto an LX Bar I want to break the bar on either side of the lantern so any Attributes are not obscured by the polyline passing through the Block.

If we are using a counterweight bar as an LX bar, then we should move it onto an appropriate Layer, as follows:

5a LX Bars Colour Cyan   LineType Continuous   LWT Default

Do this then hang a Lantern on it, again on the correct Layer:

5b Lanterns Colour Cyan   LineType Continuous   LWT Default

adding some Attribute information when prompted. Do not be afraid to zoom right in to make this easier. The insert point on the lanterns is at the hook clamp so it is easy to 'hang' them. *Fig 6.28*

Either Click Modify ➤ Break 
Or click the Break icon on the Draw toolbar

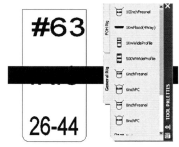

Fig 6.28 Lantern Block added in from the Tool Palette.

Break icon.

Command: _break Select object:

Pick the bar as this is what we are breaking.

```
Specify second break point or
[First point]: f ⏎
Specify first break point:
```

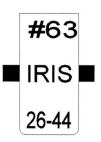

Pick a point where the bar crosses the outside of the Lantern (Perpendicular Osnap).

```
Specify second break point:
```

Pick the same point on the other side of the Lantern.

Fig 6.29 The Lantern after Break has been applied to the bar it is hanging on.

The bar is now broken on either side of the Lamp, *Fig 6.29*. Although the Bar was drawn as a polyline, after Break it is now two separate objects so you can delete any bits you do not want to show.

With a bit of practice you can make use your first pick to both define the object to break and the first break point. In this case, you just need to pick again to create the gap, having Osnap off may help this in some cases.

Group

This command allows us to create groups of items and saves having to select them either individually or switch off other layers to window them.

It is only available via the command line so type `group` to open the dialog box. *Fig 6.30*

The window at the top will list all the Groups that have been created so is currently empty. Give your Group a name and a description then click the New button in the Create Group area. This will return you to the drawing where you can pick the objects to be part of the Group. Right clicking ends the selection and the Object Grouping window reopens. The Group you just created is now in the top window.

You can add or remove objects from the group or remove (Explode) the grouping by highlighting the

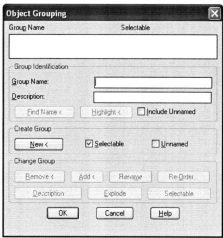

Fig 6.30 The Object Grouping (Group) dialogue.

group in the top box then using the various buttons below.

Click OK then pick any object within your group. All of them are highlighted and can now be moved, stretched scaled, deleted etc.

Hatching

Hatching fills an enclosed area with a pattern, often to show a material or simply to make a drawing clearer. Like Dimensions, Hatching is associative; if the object enclosing the Hatch alters, the Hatch will change to fill the new shape. Hatches are also Blocks in that each complete Hatch is one object.

We will fill in our walls with a concrete hatch.

Either Click Draw ➤ Hatch

Or click the Hatch icon on the Draw toolbar. *Fig 6.31.*

The Hatch dialogue appears. There are plenty of options here but we will stick with the pre-defined Hatch Patterns – so on the next box, click the Browse button to the right of the drop down arrow. *Hatching icon.*

Have a look at the various patterns and on the Other Predefined tab pick AR-CONC then OK. Leave the Angle at 0 and set the Scale to 2. Scale in Hatching is a suck-it-and-see affair. Fortunately, there is a Preview option to help you.

Now we have created the pattern we need to define the area we need to fill. There are two options: Pick Points and Select Objects.

Pick Points requires you to pick within a completely enclosed boundary. If you are successful, the boundary will change to a dashed line. If it is not in

Fig 6.31 The Hatch dialogue box.

Fig 6.32 The Hatch dialogue box–
Advanced tab showing Island detection options.

fact a closed boundary a warning will appear. In this case, you will need to use the Select Objects button and pick the lines to define the boundary. If it does Hatch is a bit more tolerant and small gaps are allowed.

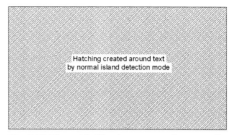

Fig 6.33 Text with Hatching using the normal island detection style.

Once you have selected the boundary, right click and a sub menu appears. Pick Preview and you will see what you will create. If you are happy right click, if not either left clicking or hitting Esc will return you to the dialogue to make alterations.

By default Hatching will detect Islands within your boundary and the Hatch will behave as shown in the dialog box, Advanced tab *Fig 6.33*. This is useful when hatching over Text as an unhatched island will appear around the text. However if this isn't what you want select the style you need and click Preview again, before applying the Hatch *Fig 6.34*.

The final tab is for creating Gradient fills, which give an impression of 3 dimensional lighting onto an object. The gradients are all in colour and you can move between a variety of different colours and orientations.

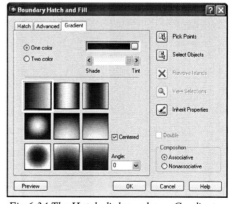

Fig 6.34 The Hatch dialogue box – Gradient fill tab and options.

Exercise 8

Hatch all the walls, creating construction lines where necessary to make enclosures. These lines can be deleted afterwards. Your drawing should look like *Fig 6.35*

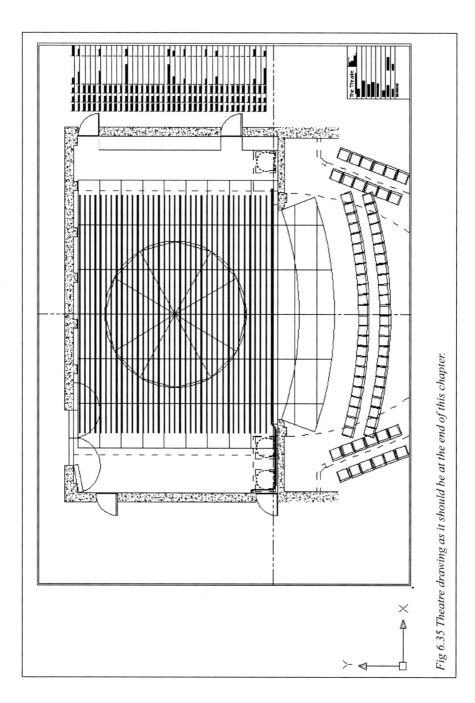

Fig 6.35 Theatre drawing as it should be at the end of this chapter.

Common problems with blocks

1 Unable to insert a Block

Tip!

Blocks can be very confusing in certain circumstances. This is especially true if you mix Blocks and drawings, which you then save to use as a block later.

On occasion, you will get this error message for what seems no good reason:

Command: _insert
Block test references itself

Invalid

What has happened is that a block named Test has been created. The drawing that the block was created in was then saved and also named Test.

This confuses AutoCAD as it seems to have a circular reference so it refuses to insert the drawing. The solution is to keep Block and drawings separate in your mind. Either have just drawings, kept in library folders, which you can then insert via DesignCenter or if you want Blocks make them part of an existing drawing or create a library drawing to hold them in. (Remember you can still get to them via the DesignCenter.)

If you are stuck then renaming the drawing causing the problem will solve it but a bit of preplanning means that you won't find yourself in this position.

2 Moving Attributes around

Another problem with Blocks is that an Attribute will clash with something else that you cannot or do not want to delete or trim. This can be frustrating, but there is a way of editing blocks in a drawing using Modify ➤ Xref and Block Editing ➤ Edit Reference in Place. But saving your changes redefines the block, meaning you are now stuck with the alterations in that block each time you use it. It may also change all the other copies of that block in the drawing.

Of course you can move any part of a Block around by Exploding it, but that negates the point of the Block. Instead, just use the Grips to grab the Attribute and move it. The exception to this is an Attribute that is Constant which as shown in *Fig B6.1* does not have a Grip.

CW 1 410 400Kg House Border 90kg

Fig B6.1 Hanging Plot showing available Grips. The constant Attribute (400kg) cannot be moved.

Fig B 6.2 shows a Birdy before and after the Attributes have been moved using Grips. Although a Block may have more than one Grip, all of it parts move together when the Move command is used.

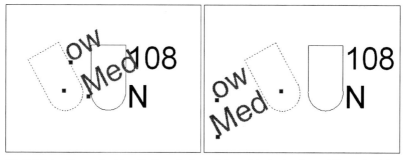

Fig B6.2 Attributes clashing (left) and after editing with the Attributes' Grips (right).

3 Nested Blocks

As we have seen Blocks of components are often created. These are used to create an object, which is then itself made into a block.

These are called nested blocks. Often they are created on individual layers so when you bring the Block into your drawing a whole load of extra layers are created. For instance a lantern may have Blocks that are the yoke and the body. That is not too bad, however there may be blocks within the block for the lock off handles, hook clamp, even the bolts, especially in a 3D drawing. Many of these Blocks may have their own attributes also so you end up importing not only extra layers but also additional blocks when all you actually want is one block for that object. *Fig B 6.3*

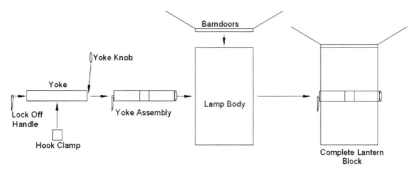

Fig B6.3 Nested Blocks adding together to make one Lantern Block.

The easiest way to get this back to one block is to firstly explode the entire drawing. You can then redefine it as a block, adding a new Base point and any attributes you need. The constituent blocks still exist so you now need to Purge them from the drawing

Click File ➤ Drawing Utilities ➤ Purge or type *purge* at the Command Line to open the window. As you can see you can get rid of a lot of clutter. Clicking on the + will reveal what you can purge under each heading. Now that you have exploded the drawing all the blocks it was made of are ready to be disposed of. *Fig B6.4*

Click Purge All if you are confident that everything available can be safely disposed of, then Close. You will be returned to the drawing, run Purge again and you will start to find

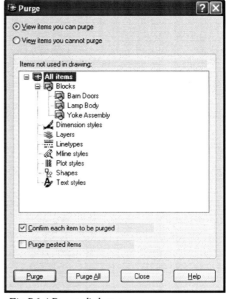

Fig B6.4 Purge dialogue.

your nested blocks. You may have to Purge several times to get them all, together with any Layers. Fig B 6.5

There is a check box on the dialog allowing you to automatically delete the nested blocks, however it is worth double-checking as some can be quite resistant to being disposed of.

When you have cleared out all the nested blocks you can now delete any unwanted details, add your own attributes and save the file as a block.

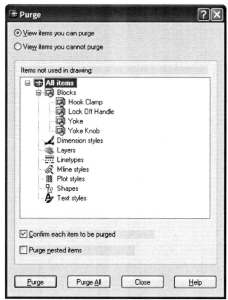

Fig B6.5 Purge dialogue revealing the nested Blocks still to be removed.

4 Blocks and Layers

Block can behave differently with layers depending on two main factors: what layers were used in their creation and which layer they are inserted into.

Generally speaking it is best to create your blocks on Layer 0. In this case it will take on the properties of whatever layer it is inserted on. This is not always possible though, especially if you have attributes as you may want to put these on separate layers to control their visibility.

In this case create the layer you anticipate inserting onto and make sure colour etc are set to ByLayer. (This is what happens when you set them up in the Layer Properties Manager.) In this case, if the Layers do not exist in the drawing, they will be created. If they already do and all the properties are the same then they will stay the same. If some are different, your block will take on those differences. You may have to change these manually back to your standard.

If you do use layer 0 to create your Blocks on then you must be vigilant in checking you are on the right Layer when inserting, otherwise you will have a lot of Properties work to do later. In the case of our Hanging Plot block it is best created on Layer 0 as when we add LX bars etc to a drawing we will want to move that bar's Block to the relevant layer to show it more clearly on the drawing.

Lanterns will or should always be on their own LX layers, even if the attributes are on different Layers they will all be LX Layers. In this case it is safe to draw the Blocks on the Layer you intend to insert them.

All this points to the importance of the drawing standard being followed through. If everybody is using the standard correctly then there will be no need for editing after insertion.

7 LINKING DRAWINGS AND OTHER FILES

Blocks place one drawing within another. Once they are inserted they become part of that drawing and changing them is quite complex, especially if you then want to reuse either version of the edited block.

On the surface External References (Xrefs) are just the same as blocks. The important difference is that when inserting an Xref on screen into another drawing, all that is actually added to the drawing is a link to the second drawing. Because the Xref is a link when you open a drawing with Xrefs in it, AutoCAD looks for the contributing drawings and opens them so that they are always the most up-to-date versions. Changes in a contributing drawing are flagged up as you open your drawing and AutoCAD loads them.

Let us look at a hypothetical CAD system in a theatre:

- The Production Manager holds the master drawings for the production
- The Designer draws the set design
- The Lighting Designer draws the LX Rig Plan

The Production Manager sets the ball rolling by creating from his template files the master drawing file: ShowMaster.dwg *Fig 7.1.*

In this drawing he has frozen some Layers that others will use, including all the Flying and LX Layers as well as any scenic Layers. He has also turned off several other Layers so that his drawing just shows the basic space.

The Set Designer starts with his own version of the theatre groundplan; it may only have the datum lines, sightlines, an indication of the stage area and

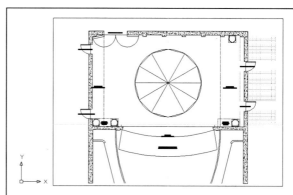

7-1 The ShowMaster drawing. This is essentially our Theatre drawing to date.

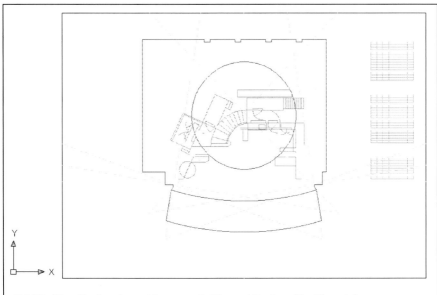

*7-2 The ShowSet drawing, with a set on it (**Corpse!** Designed by Elroy Ashmore, Haymarket Theatre, Basingstoke).*

location of the flying bars. He would draw his design over this. If he feels it is necessary he can import the theatre drawing. When finished, the set design is saved as ShowSet.dwg *Fig 7-2*.

Finally, the Lighting Designer will draw the LX Rig on his template. He will also need to see the ShowSet.dwg and possibly the ShowMaster drawings. The Lighting Designer will be using a lot of Blocks in his drawing. The LD will save his design as ShowLX.dwg *Fig 7-3*.

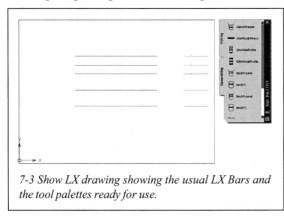

7-3 Show LX drawing showing the usual LX Bars and the tool palettes ready for use.

All of these three drawings are created from the Theatre drawing we have been drawing up to this point in the book.

We will now start to link the drawings together. When we link an external reference all we are making is a signpost for

AutoCAD to follow to find the drawings. For this reason it is important that

 a Drawings are not moved from their location once an Xref is established.

 b Any drawings that have been changed are still given the same file name.

It is also important that a convention is set up regarding Layers and the origin point. Firstly Xrefs should be inserted onto Layer 0. As noted in the previous chapter this should ensure that everything stays on the right layer when inserted. Secondly everyone should make sure that 0,0 is in the same place in each drawing. This will save a lot of tedious moving of Xrefs once they are inserted. In the case below, as each drawing is based on the same template, this is easy to do as long as you uncheck the Insertion Point – Specify Onscreen button in the dialogue box.

The first two drawings to link will be the Master to the Set drawing so that the Designer can place the scenery in relation to the space.

Open the ShowSet drawing and then click Insert ➢ External Reference to open the Select Reference File dialogue *Fig 7-4*.

This looks just the same as an ordinary Open dialogue box so pick the ShowMaster drawing and the External Reference dialogue opens. Unsurprisingly this is very similar to the Block insert window *Fig 7-5*.

7-4 Select Reference dialogue box.

The name of the drawing file is highlighted in the window with the file path below that. This display depends on your selection in the Path type drop down box. Full path is the default and it is best left as that.

The next area decides what kind of Xref this will be. An attachment will stay with the drawing, even when you then Xref this file into

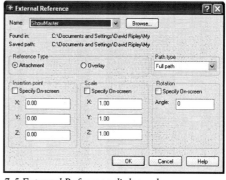

7-5 External Reference dialogue box.

another (as we will do later). Overlay only Xrefs the drawing into this one. When this drawing is then Xrefed into a subsequent drawing the overlay will be left behind.

Our ShowMaster already contains the basic outline of the building and in that the ShowSet drawing will eventually be referenced back to it we do not want the same information appearing twice. Tick the Overlay option and uncheck the Specify onscreen button under Insertion point. Finally click OK and the ShowMaster drawing appears onscreen. Switch off any Layers you do not need and then draw a few bits of scenery onstage and save the drawing *Fig 7-6*.

Next open the ShowLX drawing and create an Xref between the ShowSet drawing and ShowLX drawing. This time make it an Attachment so that the set comes in and can be part of the final Xref back to the master. When the ShowSet file is inserted into the LX drawing, the ShowMaster drawing will be left behind *Fig 7-7*.

If the Lighting Designer wants to see the rest of the theatre, then he can also Xref the ShowMaster in as an overlay. A drawing can have any number of Xrefs attached and a drawing can be used as an Xrefs as many times as

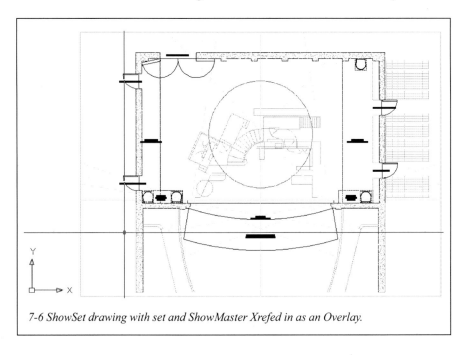

7-6 ShowSet drawing with set and ShowMaster Xrefed in as an Overlay.

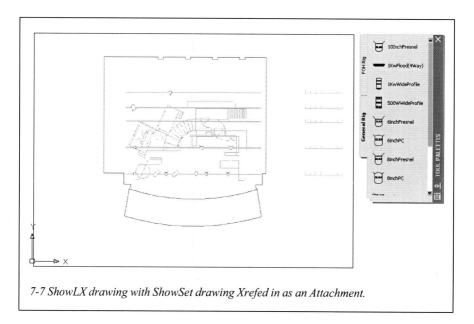

7-7 ShowLX drawing with ShowSet drawing Xrefed in as an Attachment.

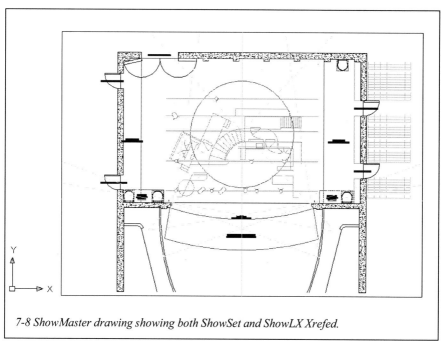

7-8 ShowMaster drawing showing both ShowSet and ShowLX Xrefed.

necessary. Remember the Xref is just a link, not the drawing itself.

We can now add a few Lanterns from our Tool Palette, remembering to change the properties of any bars etc to the right LX layer. Switch off any unused parts of the drawing and save it.

We can now open the ShowMaster drawing and Xref in the ShowLX drawing. Because this is referenced to the ShowSet drawing we need only create one Xref. We can of course set up a link to the ShowSet drawing but there is no need for this as it was Xrefed as an Attachment and thus follows through with the ShowLX drawing *Fig 7-8 (previous page)*.

A flow chart of how our various drawings link together is shown below.

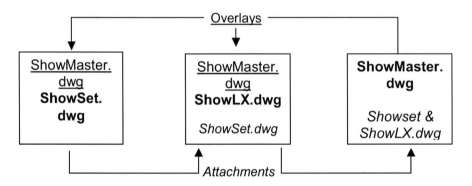

The Production Manager can now see everything in one drawing and he will be alerted if anything changes. In the bottom right corner of the screen the Manage Xrefs icon will appear whenever an Xref is present.

Click on this to open the Xref Manager *Fig 7-9*. This shows any Xrefs that are in the drawing and what type they are. If you click on the Tree View button.

Xref Manager icon.

You can see that the ShowSet drawing is part of the ShowLX drawing *Fig 7-10*.

Close this window for

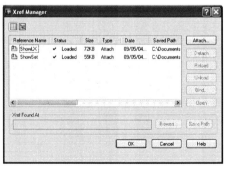

7-9 Xref Manager dialogue box.

Xref Manager – Tree display button.

now and leaving the Show Master open go into the ShowSet drawing and alter it, then save it. When you return to the ShowMaster a balloon will appear telling you of a change *Fig 7-11*. Although it will not tell you what the change is, it will at least alert you. AutoCAD checks the Xref drawings for changes every 5 minutes or so. This means that your LD can be working on his drawing at the same time your ShowMaster drawing is open. If he then saves it

7-10 Xref Manager in tree format. This setting shows more clearly the relationship between drawings.

(using the same file name) then you should get an alert to tell you that there has been a change.

This only applies however when the ShowMaster drawing (in this case) is open. If you are reopening the drawing then once it is open and the Xrefs are

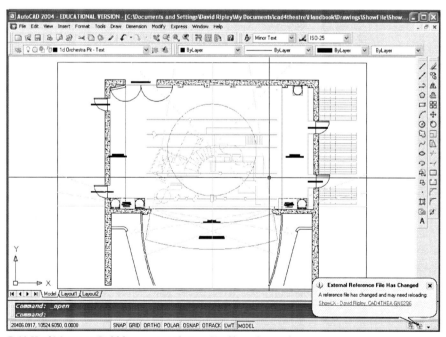

7-11 Xref Manager Bubble warning that an Xref has changed.

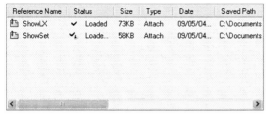

Reference Name	Status	Size	Type	Date	Saved Path
ShowLX	✔ Loaded	73KB	Attach	09/05/04...	C:\Documents
ShowSet	✔ᵢ Loade...	58KB	Attach	09/05/04...	C:\Documents

loaded open the Xref Manager to check for any alerts in the window *Fig 7-12.*

7-12 Xref Manager showing warning of a changed drawing.

To reload a drawing that has changed, highlight the drawing and click the Reload button. Once a show has finished then all the drawings can be pulled together to create one drawing file. To do this, again highlight the drawings and click Bind. This should only be done once you are certain you have finished with the drawings!

The Bind function changes your Xref into a Block and therefore part of the drawing. As with Blocks the original contributing drawings still exist and can be archived separately.

7-13 Bind Xref dialogue box.

There are two choices of the way drawings are bound once you have started the Bind process from the Xref Manager. A dialogue box appears *Fig 7-13.* with a choice of Bind or Insert. The differences mainly affect how Layers are shown in the drawing.

When Bind is used the Layers from the contributing drawing are shown in the format *Drawing Name1$0$Layer Name.* If a Layer Name already exists the 0 will change to 1 *Fig 7-14.*

When Insert is used then any Layers named the same merge. Any new layers just take on an ordinary Layer Name without any reference to the source drawing.

It will be worth trying to get your designers to add notes in the revisions sections of the Title box or send you an email detailing changes as well. Otherwise

7-14 Layer manager after Binding Xrefs with the Bind method.

you may spend some time trying to identify the improvements. Alternatively they can use the Revision Cloud tool but this should be used sparingly otherwise the parts of the drawing you want to see may eventually disappear under the weight of changes to the design.

Revision Cloud

This tool draws a curly line which, when it is close enough, will form an enclosed shape. You can then insert your text, noting the revision in the normal way. It is also rather good for drawing trees, bushes and other foliage! *Fig 7-15.*

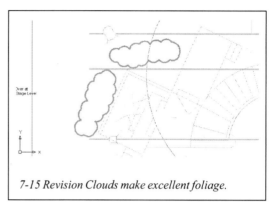

7-15 Revision Clouds make excellent foliage.

Either Click Draw ➤ Revision Cloud

or Click the RevCloud Icon on the Draw Toolbar

or Type revcloud ↵ at the Command line.

The command line will read

```
Command: revcloud
Minimum arc length: 15    Maximum arc
length: 15
Specify start point or [Arc length/
Object] <Object>:
```

Revision Cloud (Rev Cloud) icon.

Type A so that we can change the Arc length as it is too small at the moment. I have changed it to 375 (15 x 25), but do experiment, especially if you are drawing foliage.

```
Specify minimum length of arc <15>: 375
Specify maximum length of arc <375>: ↵
Specify start point or [Object] <Object>:
```

Click in the drawing area to start the RevCloud

```
Guide crosshairs along cloud path...
```

So do as you are told and create your cloud, remembering to close the shape. Once you are close enough to the start of the line the RevCloud will

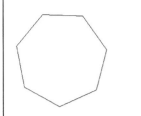  

7-16 Revision Cloud applied to an object. Left to Right; the original polygon, after RevCloud is applied and after the direction the RevCloud runs has been reversed.

snap to it. At this point your command line will show

`Revision cloud finished.`

Hitting Enter at any point before the RevCloud is closed will give you an open-ended shape, which may be useful on occasion.

If you use the Object option then you can convert an existing, closed Polyline to a Rev Cloud just by clicking on it. The command line then offers you

`Select object: Reverse direction [Yes/No] <No>:`

If you answer yes then the way the arcs of the Rev Cloud run will be reversed *Fig 7-16.*

Layers in Xrefs

As you can imagine having several drawings linked means a lot of Layers. Once a drawing is Xrefed in its Layers appear in the Layer Properties Manager in the format *Drawing name|LayerName Fig 7-17.*

The Layers are also greyed out, although they can be edited. Any changes are only shown on the drawing you are currently using and are not written back to the Xref. However by default those changes will remain even if you reload the Xref.

Obviously you cannot change properties on part of an Xref by clicking on it because, just as Blocks

7-17 Layer Manager with unbound Xrefs inserted. The greyed out Layers are from the contributing drawings.

do, they act as one entity regardless of how many contributing objects they are made from.

Xrefs, as with Blocks, can be edited in place using Modify ➤ Xref and Block Editing ➤ Edit Reference in Place. This is quite a complicated procedure and the point of linking these drawings together is that only the designers make the changes so you know that the drawing is up to date and correct. I therefore do not recommend using this 'master override' editing tool. Apart from it negating the Xref system it will probably cause quite a lot of ill feeling if one person decides to start deleting or moving parts of someone else's design. It is important that the designers and other contributors to the drawings retain ownership of them. This helps ensure that everyone really is looking at the current state of play, rather than debating which version the team should work to, as is often the case.

Inserting Images

At some point you may want to insert a graphic into your AutoCAD drawing. This is most likely to be the Theatre's logo or perhaps that of the show or producing company.

These Raster images are treated by AutoCAD as Xrefs and work the same way.

Click Insert ➤ Raster Image

Or Type `imageattach` at the command line

A browse dialogue box appears. Find your Image and select it as you would any file.

Insert Image icon.

If you Click the Image icon on the Draw Toolbar (to access this if it isn't visible click on the black triangle on the bottom right corner of the Insert Icon. Hold the button down while the sub toolbar pops out, then select Image) *Fig 7-18* then the Image Manager *Fig 7-19* will open. Click on the Attach button and this will open the same browse dialogue as above.

7-18 The Insert pop out menu showing from left to right Insert; Block, Xref, Image, Import File and OLE Object.

7-19 Image Manager dialogue box.

Once you have selected your Image file, then another dialogue box opens which is very similar to the Xref Insert dialogue box *Fig 7-20*. Insert the Image as you have done with Block or Xrefs. By default the specify onscreen option is selected for both position and scale so the command line sequence will look like this:

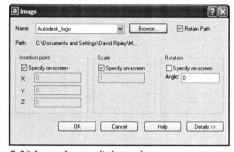

7-20 Insert Image dialogue box.

```
Command: _imageattach
Specify insertion point <0,0>:
Select a point
Base image size: Width:
2.830000, Height: 2.120000,
Millimeters
Specify scale factor <1>:
```

As the image is very small you will need to change the scale. Start with a scale of 100. You can then resize it using the blue handles that appear after insertion Fig *7-21*.

Once the image has been attached most editing functions work as they would with any object, the exception being commands such as scale where the aspect ratio of the object is always maintained. There are several options in the Modify ➤ Object ➤ Image to adjust the actual raster image.

7-21 Title Block with a company logo inserted; a lot of resizing was required to get this to fit.

Adjust Once you have selected an Image then a dialogue will open, allowing changes to Brightness, Contrast and Fade to be made *Fig 7-22*.

Quality This is a global command affecting all Images in a drawing.

The options are shown at the command line and are High or Draft You normally only need this command if AutoCAD is running

7-22 Image Adjust dialogue.

slowly due to a lot of High quality Images. In any case this will not affect print quality of the image, which is always high.

Transparency In some formats you can use this so that the Drawing will show through the Image. Again this is set at the command line and is a simple on or off.

Frame When a Raster Image is inserted it is contained within a frame. The frame has the properties of the Layer that it was inserted on and is used by AutoCAD to select the Image for editing. You can turn off the frame when you have completed editing it but once it is gone it is difficult to do any more editing as you have nothing to select the image with.

Luckily you don't need to select the image to turn the frame on or off, which is done at the command line.

Linking to Other Files

Of course, it may be there are other files as well as images that you need to add to an AutoCAD drawing. You may wish to add tables showing parts for instance that have been created in Excel (this could be attribute extract information) or some simple notation created in Word.

There are three ways to insert information from other programs into AutoCAD.

Paste

Often you can just Cut (Ctrl + X) or Copy (Ctrl + C) in the original application and then Paste (Ctrl + V) in AutoCAD or from the icons on the Standard toolbar. The OLE Properties dialogue will open allowing you to adjust the size and scale of the object. You can also use the blue handles on the object to resize *Fig 7-23*.

Using this method, there is no link to the original program so if what you have pasted changes, you will need to Cut and Paste again.

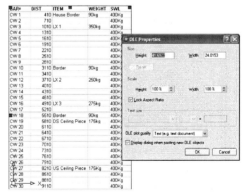

7-23 OLE Properties dialogue and the object it is referring to, in this case an Excel file created from Attributes.

Link

This method keeps the external file linked so that when it changes, that is reflected in AutoCAD. Again you would just Cut or Copy the object to the Clipboard.

In AutoCAD you then select Edit ➤ Paste Special to open a dialogue box, then select Paste Link and OK *Fig 7-24*.

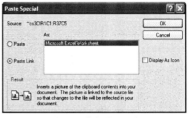

7-24 Paste Special dialogue box.

Embed

Embedded objects can also be linked but if you then double click them in AutoCAD this will launch the file's program so that it can be edited.

To create an Embedded object Click Insert ➤ OLE Object and a dialogue will

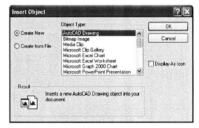

7-25 Insert Object dialogue.

open *Fig 7-25*. You now have a choice of opening an existing file or creating a new one. To use a current file choose Select from file and then navigate to your file. Double click it or use Open, then when you are returned to the dialogue box you can check the Link box so that the object automatically updates. Click OK and the OLE properties dialogue opens as the object appears in the drawing. Resize if you want or just click OK again to finishing inserting.

If you want to create a new object then select the program that you want to create a file in, which will launch that program, add in your data and then save and close it. How this is done will vary according to application. Again, when you return to AutoCAD the OLE Properties dialogue will be open. Click OK to insert your data.

Exercise 9

Open the Lamp drawing. It is currently blank, but has the correct blocks to create the Fresnel lantern shown.

Build the lamp and then extract the attributes. Once you have done that you can edit the Excel file if you wish.

Next insert the Excel file into the drawing as shown: choose any of the methods outlined.

You should produce something similar to *Fig Ex 9*.

Lamp Parts List		
Block Name	Count	PART#
LampAssembly	1	Lamp Assembly
Yoke	1	Yoke
LockOffHandle	1	1 Lock Off Handle
Barndoors	1	Barndoors
Yoke Handle	1	Yoke Handle

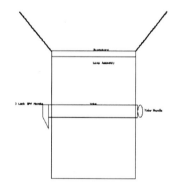

Exchanging linked drawings

Naturally you will want to send drawings, which will be either Xrefed or have an Image as part of the drawing. Remember, in both cases you have created a link to where the files are kept. Therefore, if you move the file the links are broken.

If the drawings are Xrefed then by using the Bind function in the Xref Manager you will add all the drawings together and can then send them to someone else with all the parts intact. Alternatively, all the contributing files can be sent and the links reestablished. If this isn't done correctly then the Xref manager will show an error message *Fig 7-26*.

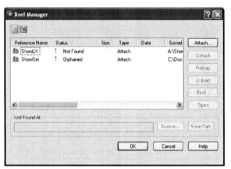

7-26 Xref Manger, the files shown have been moved from their location causing an error message.

Unfortunately, to send an image with a drawing is more complicated as the Bind function is not available. In this case you will need to send the image as well as the drawing. If you are using a floppy disc or other media, then you will need to save both drawing and image on the disc then reset the path to the image so that when AutoCAD opens the drawing it will look on the disc for the image. Your recipient can then either use the files from the media or save it onto the hard drive and reset the path accordingly.

If the files are not included then when the drawing is opened where the image should be, a box will be shown with the Image's original file path shown in it *Fig 7-27*.

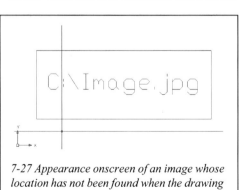

7-27 Appearance onscreen of an image whose location has not been found when the drawing was opened.

Setting up an Xref File system.

Tip!

Ideally all drawings that are to be linked together should be held on a central server. This would mean that access could be controlled so that rights to edit drawings are restricted whilst most people could view them. However, not being in a network does not restrict your use of Xrefs and ensuring the drawings are up to date. As long as a drawing that is emailed or supplied on a disk is saved with the same file name in the same location then the Xref will find it and use it.

When drawings are altered it is recommended that the file name has an incremental number or date added to it i.e. ShowSet 1.dwg, ShowSet 2.dwg or ShowLX 27-07-04, ShowLX 28-07-04 etc. This allows you to track what changes have been made if necessary. At the end of each session, however a final save should be made using the specified file name, ShowSet.dwg for example. This 'End of Day' file will have all the cumulative changes and will still link into the other drawings it is referenced to.

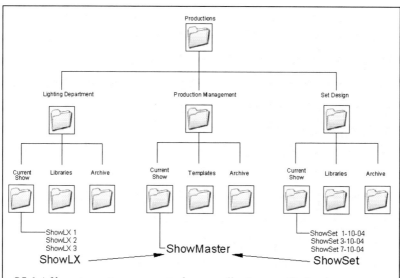

B7-1 A file system set up on a central server, allowing easy Xrefing between departments as well as archiving of past projects and libraries of blocks.

This system can equally apply to other drawing programs that may be used in a theatre for lighting or set design. As long as the 'End of Day' file can be saved as a compatible AutoCAD drawing then it too can be Xrefed in, whilst the designer can continue to work in his native file format.

Within this area, templates and libraries can also be held. For the illustration *Fig B7-1*. I have only shown LX and Set but obviously this can be expanded to any department using CAD and who needs to have their work and its potential impact on a common drawing. This is particularly important for large-scale productions where departments such as Sound and Stage Technology can have a considerable impact.

8 DRAWING IN THREE DIMENSIONS

Until now, we have concentrated on 2D drawing, which is the kind we normally work in for Plans, construction drawings etc. Sometimes however it is useful to look at something from a different angle and model it in 3D. AutoCAD can create great-looking 3D Models which when rendered can look most realistic. It is however a lengthy and complicated process to firstly create the model, then apply the materials to it, light it and finally render it. This will be of necessity a cursory look at three dimensional modelling, as it could occupy a book as a subject in itself.

Drawing in 3D is a different skill from drawing in 2D and a great deal of spatial awareness is required as it involves moving our origin (the UCS) around quite a lot. You can only undertake certain functions, particularly when editing objects when you have the XY plane correctly orientated for that action.

There are three basic kinds of 3D drawing we will look at: Drawing in the Z Axis, Extruding 2D Shapes into 3D Shapes, and Modelling with Solids. Of these, only Drawing in the Z Axis is available to users of AutoCAD LT. Although 3D Solids can be read in AutoCAD LT, they cannot be created or edited. Similarly, the Extrude function is also not included in this version of AutoCAD, nor are any rendering features, although hidden and restricted shaded views can be created, from existing drawing containing solids or surfaces. This lack of 3D functionality explains the large price difference between the two versions and how much 3D work you are likely to undertake should be considered prior to purchase.

Open up your Theatre drawing and turn off all the layers except the one your theatre's walls are on. As we have discussed before, coordinates are dependant on two axes, X, which runs horizontally across our screen and Y running vertically across the same plane. The Z axis which we are about to use runs from our screen towards us *Fig 8-1*. To enter a coordinate using this axis three numbers are required in the format X,Y,Z.

8-1 Z, the third axis runs towards you from the XY plane which, in Plan view is across your screen.

Drawing in the Z Axis

Create a new Layer for our 3D drawing; it is the same as the current walls one except the name should read 1b Structure-3D Walls. Create the new Layer by clicking on the 1b Structure – Walls layer – then click New. The resultant layer is based upon the highlighted one so now all you need to do is change the name. Start the Line command and as a start point pick the corner shown in *Fig 8-2*.

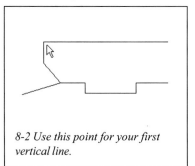

8-2 Use this point for your first vertical line.

When you are asked for an endpoint enter the following

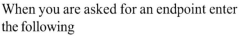

```
Specify next point or
[Undo]: @0,0,8000
```

Finish the command. The drawing looks unchanged so click View ➤ 3D Views ➤ SW Isometric and you should now see your line extending up from the drawing. Either copy the line around the other parts of the prosc wall or draw them as before, then join the tops together. Your drawing should look like this *Fig 8-3*. You can do this in the Isometric view, if you want to go back to the Plan view click View ➤ 3D Views ➤ Plan View ➤ then either Current or World UCS. Alternatively you can change the point of view to one of the other options in the View ➤ 3D Views menu.

Notice how the Crosshairs stay in the current XY plane, making them look a bit odd. They are a useful reference as to where you are on the drawing and as you change views they will change also according to the orientation of the UCS.

You have now drawn in 3D, however you have not created a 3 Dimensional object, just a series of lines. No surfaces have been created, just what is a simple wireframe model.

To see the difference between drawing lines in 3D and creating objects we will now extrude part of our current drawing.

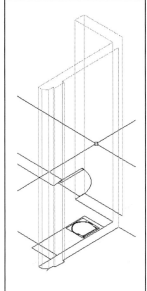

8-3 The prosc wall created from lines draw in the Z axis.

Extruding

We will use another part of our existing drawing, the next section of wall on stage left. As this is a simple rectangle, so again trace over it in a contrasting colour using the Rectangle option, or a Polyline.

Extrude requires an enclosed Polyline to work so bear this in mind when attempting this command. Now you have your shape to extrude, start the command

Either Click Draw ➤ Solids ➤ Extrude

or Type extrude ↵ at the Command line

    Command: extrude

    Current wire frame density:
    ISOLINES=4

    Select objects: Pick the
    Rectangle 1 found

    Select objects: ↵

    Specify height of extrusion or
    [Path]: 8000

    Specify angle of taper for
    extrusion <0>: ↵

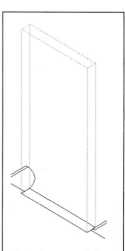

8-4 The ground plan wall section extruded into a 3D shape.

Your rectangle will now become a box. This is a true 3D object in that it has height, width and depth *Fig 8-4*. As you can see from the Taper option, we could have made a more interesting shape. Feel free to have a play before moving on.

You can see that it has become a solid by trying a couple of simple commands on it.

Either Click View ➤ Shade ➤ Hidden

or Type hide ↵ at the Command line

Whereas before you could see the whole wireframe of your box, now it shows itself as a solid, so the lines furthest from you are hidden *Fig 8-5*. Now try this:

Either Click View ➤ Shade ➤ then any of the bottom four Shaded options

or Type shade ↵ at the Command line.

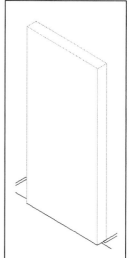

8-5 The same shape with 'Hide' activated. Note how the rear lines have disappeared.

The box is now coloured in and you can clearly see it through our first set of 3D lines. You can also see that it is lit as some faces are in shadow. All in all it looks a much more realistic 3 Dimensional image. The appearance of the UCS has also changed so that it is a 3D object with the axes colour coded *Fig 8-6*.

Modelling with Solids

3D Solids are created by using standard shapes and then editing them. These shapes are Box, Sphere, Cylinder, Cone, Wedge and Torus *Fig 8-7*. We will mainly use the Box command but using combinations of these primitives and then by adding and subtracting parts from each other most shapes can be created.

We will carry on moving upstage and creating our walls. Box works in many way like the Extrude command: firstly you define the bottom of the box then its height. To draw this object you will probably need to change the view. I used the NW Isometric view. Look at the UCS once you are in this view.

Either Click Draw ➤ Solids ➤ Box

8-6 The wall section with 'Shade' applied. The object uses the layer colour.

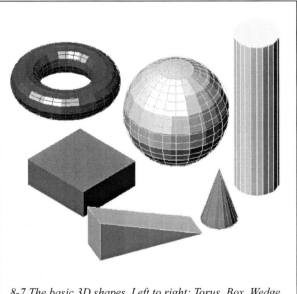

8-7 The basic 3D shapes. Left to right; Torus, Box, Wedge, Sphere, Cone, Cylinder.

or Type box ⏎ at the Command line

```
Command: box
Specify corner of
box or [CEnter]
<0,0,0>:
Specify corner or
[Cube/Length]:
```

Create a rectangle to form the base of the box so that it butts up to our extrusion and right up to the US corner of the wall. This means you will go over the doorway but for now do not worry about that.

8-8 Next wall section created by making a Box. Note the line where it meets the previous section.

8-9 The corner section added.

```
Specify height: 8000 ⏎
```

Your box will be created just as the extrusion was *Fig 8-8*.

Now fill in the next section as shown *Fig 8-9*.

As noted above we have just covered over our doorway. We need to remove a section of the wall to recreate it, also we want to make the sections of wall we have just created into one object. To do this we need to use the Solids Editing commands.

Editing Solids

Much of the creating of solids is achieved by creating simple shapes and then combining them or removing parts of them to form more complex objects. These editing tools will help you create many objects but the order of doing things may need planning.

Union

Our first job is to join all our current sections together so they are one.

Either Click Draw ➤ Solids Editing ➤ Union

or Type union ⏎ at the Command line

```
Command: union
```

Pick our three boxes. You will need to pick the wireframe lines to select

them; the bits in the middle don't count.

```
Select objects: 1 found
Select objects: 1 found, 2 total
Select objects: 1 found, 3 total
Select objects: ↵
```

Any line between the boxes should now have disappeared and they are one object *Fig 8-10*. You can do this with any number of solids of any shape to create other objects.

8-10 The three sections have now been joined using Union.

Subtract

We are now going to create the doorway. To do this we firstly need to make a box that is doorway shaped, then remove it from the wall.

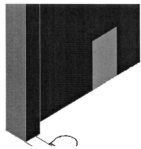

Switch off the layer you created the 3D walls on and make a box, which is the size of the doorway and 2000 high on a different Layer. Make sure that you can see it when you turn your walls back on *Fig 8-11*.

Either Click Draw ➤ Solids Editing ➤ Subtract or Type subtract ↵ at the Command line

8-11 Another Box is used to create the shape of the doorway.

```
Command: subtract
Select solids and regions to
subtract from ..
```

Pick the object you want left after subtraction, in this case the wall

```
Select objects: 1 found
Select objects: ↵
Select solids and regions to
subtract ..
```

Pick the box we have just created in the doorway

```
Select objects: 1 found
Select objects:
```

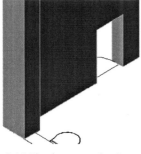

8-12 The doorway after being subtracted from the rest of the wall section.

The doorway will now be removed as shown in *Fig 8-12*.

Intersect

Intersect works in the same way as subtract by removing parts of solids. However in this case all that is left is the area where the two objects crossed.

On a new page try this

Firstly type `isolines` at the command line

```
Command: isolines
Enter new value for ISOLINES <4>: 24
```

This will make your solids' wireframes denser and clearer.

We will draw a Sphere and Torus (a ring doughnut) that intersect, then edit them and see what we get.

Either Click Draw ➤ Solids ➤ Sphere

or Type `sphere` ↵ at the Command line

```
Command: sphere
Current wire frame density:  ISOLINES=24
Specify center of sphere <0,0,0>:850,500  ↵
Specify radius of sphere or [Diameter]: 150  ↵
```

The sphere is created, switch to the SW Iso view and then start the Torus command.

Either Click Draw ➤ Solids ➤ Torus

or Type `torus` ↵ at the Command line

```
Command: torus
Current wire frame density:  ISOLINES=24
Specify center of torus <0,0,0>: 850,500  ↵
Specify radius of torus or [Diameter]: 175  ↵
Specify radius
of tube or
[Diameter]: 50  ↵
```

You should now have a drawing that looks like *Fig 8-13* (I have put Hide on for clarity). We can now start the Intersect command.

Either Click Draw ➤ Solids

Editing ➤ Intersect

or Type `intersect` ↵ at

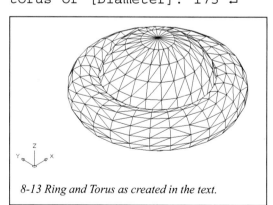

8-13 Ring and Torus as created in the text.

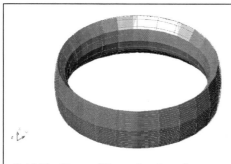

8-14 The Ring and Torus drawing after Intersect has been used.

the Command line

```
Command: intersect
```

Pick both objects

```
Select objects: 1
found
Select objects: 1
found, 2 total
Select objects: ↵
```

As you can see we now have a very narrow wedding ring type torus *Fig 8-14*. As you can also see a bit of foresight and planning is required to use this tool!

Wedges

Unsurprisingly, Wedges are shaped like a piece of cheese. The order of picking when creating the base of your wedge is vital; otherwise, you will have to start again

Start a new drawing then:

Either

Click Draw ➢ Solids ➢ Wedge or Type wedge ↵ at the Command line, which will then read:

```
WEDGE
Specify first corner of wedge or [CEnter]
<0,0,0>: 500,250 ↵
```

This is an important selection. The high part of the wedges ramp will be at the point you now select running along the Y axis.

```
Specify corner or [Cube/Length]: @400,200 ↵
```

This corner defines which way the wedge runs as well as its base. Move from your first pick left and the ramp goes that way – to the right and that is the bottom.

```
Specify height: 100 ↵
```

This is the highest point of the wedge.

Your wedge is now created; switch to an isometric view to see it in all its glory *Fig 8-15*.

Try creating wedges with different start and endpoints for the base so that you are familiar with the creation process.

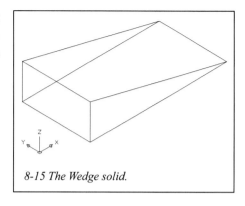

8-15 The Wedge solid.

Exercise

Complete the rest of the back wall including creating the gap for the dock doors, which are 4.5 metres high. You can also create the open dock doors. Remember all the normal editing tools also apply to solids, so do not be afraid to try them.

Your target is shown in *Fig Ex 10* below.

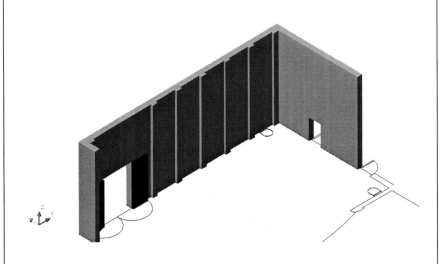

Drawing at Height

When drawing the galleries in we need to put them at the height specified on the groundplan: the perch at 3100 and the Fly floor at 6500.

We can move the UCS so that the origin is at these heights. The trouble with this is that as soon as we use the drawing to reference the size of the galleries and use Osnap then the box will end up at the level of the lines, which is of course at our stage level.

Instead, we should draw the Galleries on the stage floor and then move the galleries up to the right height. Using the methods outlined above, create the SL perch. If you wish you can remove the traps for the access ladders. The galleries should have a depth of 100 -150.

Once you have created the perch (remember to create a 3D layer) we will make the screen a bit more interesting by dividing it in two with a different view on each side.

Click View ➢ Viewports ➢ 2 Viewports. The command line will show:

```
Command: _vports

Enter an option [Save/Restore/Delete/Join/
SIngle/?/2/3/4] <3>: _2

Enter a configuration option [Horizontal/
Vertical] <Vertical>: Type v ↵

Regenerating model.
```

Your screen will split into two *Fig 8-16.*

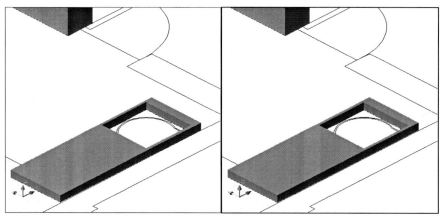

8-16 Viewports – Two Vertical viewports have been created.

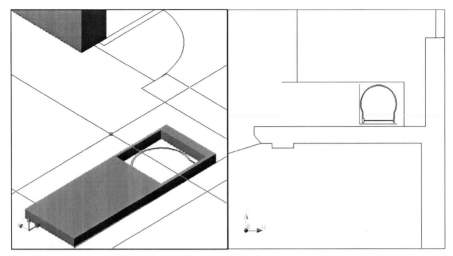

8-17 Two Viewports with a different View in each. This is very useful when creating 3D objects.

Clicking in either screen makes it active. You will see the crosshairs and the border will be black on whichever is active.

Click in either screen then change that view to Plan as outlined earlier. Your screen should now look like *Fig 8-17*.

Now move into the other screen and start the Move command.

```
Command: move
Select objects: 1 found I am using my perch
Select objects: ↵
Specify base point or displacement:
```

Make sure you use the bottom of the perch for the base point as the height is to the underside of the perch

```
Specify second point of displacement or
<use first point as displacement>:@0,0,3100 ↵
```

You will see the perch move in the Isometric view; in the plan view it will not appear to as it is only moving vertically. Splitting the screen like this is useful as it gives you two references when editing objects.

Now you can create your flyfloor. In the plan viewport make a box using the Endpoint Osnaps shown in *Fig 8-18* overleaf.

Oops! You will probably end up with *Fig 8-19* below. This is because you have selected Endpoints on differing planes. In this case it is better to use the Isometric view and if possible switch off any Layers that may cause problems. Create your Flyfloor and then move it as before but this time 6500 up. Your drawing should now look like *Fig 8-20*.

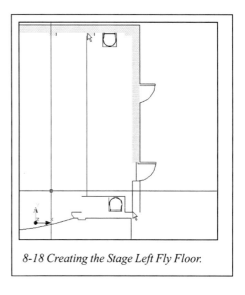

8-18 Creating the Stage Left Fly Floor.

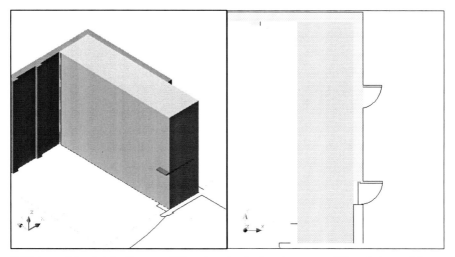

8-19 A possible mistake. Because different parts of a drawing are on different planes, it is sometimes difficult to see where an Osnap is. In this case an Osnap at the top of the wall and another on the groundplan have been picked when defining the base of a Box.

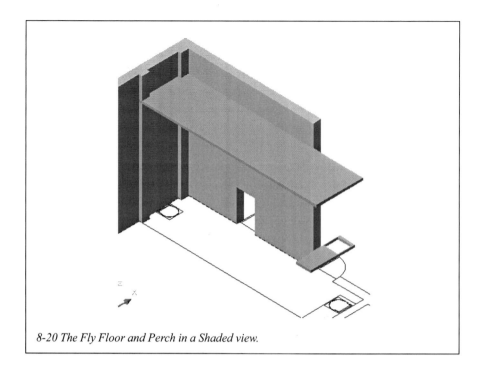

8-20 The Fly Floor and Perch in a Shaded view.

Moving the UCS

It is often necessary in 3D work to move the UCS to a different plane. This may not only involve moving it up or down but also rotating it so that XY may be at 90° to the normal position.

To show this let us create a flying bar. Firstly on your plan we will draw a Cylinder so we are familiar with the command sequence

```
Command: cylinder
Current wire frame density: ISOLINES24
Specify center point for base of cylinder or
[Elliptical] <0,0,0>:
```

Pick any point

```
Specify radius for base of cylinder or
[Diameter]: 24.2 ↵
Specify height of cylinder or [Center of
other end]: 12500 ↵
```

Now because the final dimension or value is the Z value the bar is sitting on the stage vertically, in other words it is a boom *Fig 8-21*. To turn it horizontally is rather complex so instead we will re orientate the drawings UCS so we can draw the 3D bars over the current bar lines

Turn on the Flying bars layer so that we can see them. We will now move the UCS in stages, first we will move it to the end of the first bar. I am using the Isometric view as it is easier to check what you are doing.

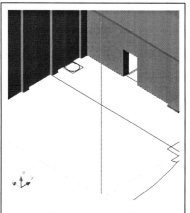

8-21 Cylinder created to the size of a flying bar.

Type UCS at the command line

```
Command: ucs ↵
Current ucs name:   *TOP*
Enter an option [New/Move/orthoGraphic/Prev/
Restore/Save/Del/Apply/?/World]
<World>: m ↵
Specify new origin point or [Zdepth]<0,0,0>:
```

Pick the Endpoint of the downstage bar *Fig 8-22*.

Now we need to rotate the UCS so that X plane is running up and down stage whilst the Y plane points toward the grid.

Pick Tools ➤ New UCS ➤ Z. The command line will read:

```
Command: _ucs
Current ucs name:   *TOP*
Enter an option [New/
Move/orthoGraphic/Prev/
Restore/Save/Del/Apply/
?/World]
<World>: _z
Specify rotation angle
about Z axis <90>:
```

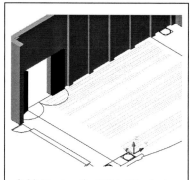

8-22 Moving the UCS. The first move is to the end of a flying bar.

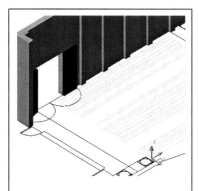

8-23 Next The UCS is rotated around the Z axis.

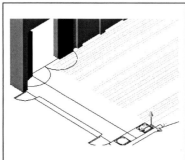

8-24 Now it is rotated around the X axis.

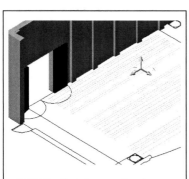

8-25 Finally it is moved to the height required.

Enter –90 to rotate the UCS around the Z Axis 90° clockwise *Fig 8-23.*

Now click Pick Tools ➢ New UCS ➢ X again the command line changes

```
Command: _ucs
Current ucs name: *NO
NAME*
Enter an option [New/
Move/orthoGraphic/Prev/
Restore/Save/Del/Apply/
?/World]
<World>: _x
Specify rotation angle
about X axis <90>:
```

This time accept the default and the UCS will now be orientated correctly *Fig 8-24.*

Lastly we need to move the UCS vertically. I have chosen to move it 8250 up. You now need to take special note of the orientation of the UCS. Normally to raise an object the coordinates would be 0,0,8250. As we have moved the UCS our Y axis is now pointing upwards, so our coordinate will be 0,8250,0.

```
Command: ucs
Current ucs name:   *NO
NAME*
Enter an option [New/
Move/orthoGraphic/Prev/
Restore/Save/Del/Apply/
?/World]
<World>: m ⏎
Specify new origin point
or [Zdepth]<0,0,0>:
0,8250,0  Fig 8-25.
```

We can now draw our bar

```
Command: cylinder
Current wire frame
density:
ISOLINES24
Specify center
point for base of
cylinder or
[Elliptical]
<0,0,0>:
Accept this
default
Specify radius for base of cylinder or
[Diameter]: 24.2
Specify height of cylinder or [Center of
other end]: -12500
```

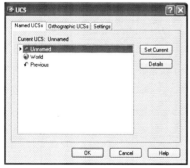

8-26 Flying bar created using the UCS in the correct orientation.

Note the minus figure. And here it is in *Fig 8-26*.

Now that you have spent the time moving the UCS you should save it for future use. Click Tools ➤ Named UCS and a dialogue box will open *Fig 8-27*. Double click in the Unnamed box and change the name to Bars then click.

If you re-open the dialogue then you can switch between any UCS you have created, plus the WCS (World).

In the same dialogue box is another tab Orthographic UCSs *Fig 8-28*. This holds some basic UCS positions which you will find useful. However, in the

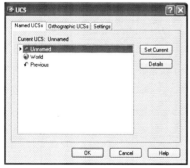

8-27 The UCS dialogue box, Named UCS tab.

8-28 The UCS dialogue box, Orthographic UCS tab.

case above you would still need to move the UCS so that your origin is in the right place to draw the bar.

As you can see from creating our flying bar, it is important to have an acute awareness of the UCS and what plane you are working in. In the above case, because of how we need to create a cylinder, our Z axis has been transposed to become the Y axis. In this case we wanted to raise the bar, which is normally the Z axis, but because of our placement of the UCS the normal X,Y,Z coordinate input would have actually moved it off stage left.

Editing functions take place along the XY plane so for instance if we wanted to rotate our bar so it ran diagonally across the stage we would use the World UCS. Using the split screen helps spot mistakes, as what looks correct in Plan may actually look very different in another view.

Rendering

Rendering is the application of materials and lighting to our model. In the early days of CAD a teapot was the first

8-29 The Render Toolbar.

object rendered and as a result the icon for rendering is a green teapot. You can open the Render toolbar by right clicking in a blank area of another toolbar, then selecting Render *Fig 8-29.*

The first thing is to import any materials you wish to apply to your model from the library. We will render the back wall with a brick material, then shine some lights on it.

Either Click View ➤ Render ➤ Materials Library

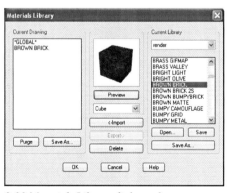

8-30 Materials Library dialogue box.

or Click the Materials Library Icon on the Render Toolbar

Materials Library Icon.

or Type matlib ↵ at the Command Line.

This opens the dialogue *Fig 8-30.* On the right is the library: scroll down and highlight Brown Brick. Next in the Preview area select Cube (the default is Sphere), then click Preview and you will get an idea of what the material looks like.

Now click Import and the Material will be copied to the left hand pane. It is now available to be used in our drawing. Exit the dialogue box and then:

Either Click View ➤ Render ➤ Materials

 or Click the Materials Icon on the Render Toolbar

Materials Icon. or Type rmat ⏎ at the Command Line.

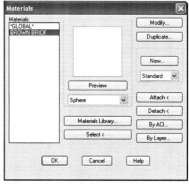

8-31 Materials dialogue box.

Another dialogue box opens *Fig 8-31*. Before using the material we need to edit it slightly as the bricks are rather small. Click Modify and a new dialogue is shown, *Fig 8-32*. By using the radio buttons we can alter all of these various attributes of the materials basic bitmap. With the Color/Pattern button active click Adjust Bitmap. In the next dialogue, click the button marked Fit to Object in the Map Style area *Fig 8-33*. Return to the Materials by clicking OK and OK again in the next box.

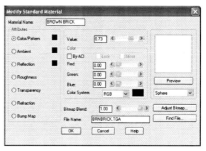

8-32 Modify Standard Material dialogue box.

Materials are attached to Solids by three methods:

Attach

Using attach you simply pick the object you wish to apply the material to. Click the Attach button, and the command line will read:

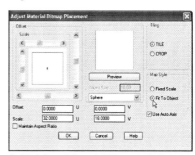

8-33 Adjust Material Bitmap dialogue box.

    _RMAT

    Gathering objects...0 found

    Select objects to attach "BROWN BRICK" to:

Pick all the objects that make up the back wall

    1 found

```
Select objects:  ⏎
Updating drawing...done.
```

By ACI

ACI stands for AutoCAD Color Index. You will select a colour from the dialogue box and every instance of an object with that colour will have the material attached *Fig 8-34.*

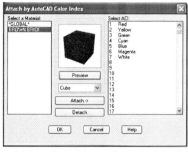

8-34 Attaching Materials using the ACI dialogue box.

By Layer

Obviously, you can select a Layer and everything on the Layer will have the materials attached. If you are using this method, a lot of extra, specific Layers will be required *Fig 8-35.*

Whichever method you use the drawing will remain the same. Before we can see the materials we need to render the drawing.

Rendering

Either Click View ➤ Render ➤ Render

or Click the Render Icon on the Render Toolbar

8-35 Attaching Materials using the Layer dialogue box.

or Type render ⏎ at the Command Line.

The dialogue box has a lot of options on it *Fig 8-36.* For us the main ones are:

The Render Icon.

Rendering Type is Photo Real (because we have a material applied).

Rendering Options are Smooth Shade and Apply Materials Destination is the Viewport: that is we will see it in the AutoCAD drawing area.

Once you are sure all these are correct, click Render. For this drawing this should

8-36 The Render dialogue box.

be quite a quick process, a few seconds, however the more materials etc you have the longer it will take.

You should have a drawing that looks like *Fig 8-37*. If you want to zoom in, then you will have to Render again once you have done so.

There are two other options when rendering your image under the Destination heading. The first is the Render Window, which will create a Bitmap (.bmp) file. This opens a separate window on top of AutoCAD *Fig 8-38*.

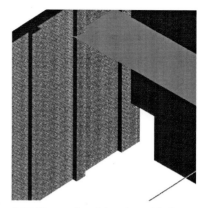

8-37 The rendered drawing with the Brown Brick Material on the walls.

File allows you to save the render in a small variety of formats: again the default is .bmp, but using the More Options button opens a new dialogue box: File Output Configuration *Fig 8-39*. Select your preferred file type and any other options, and then click OK to return to the Render dialogue.

Once you have successfully rendered your drawing, apply a material to the galleries and dock doors you have drawn and render the drawing again

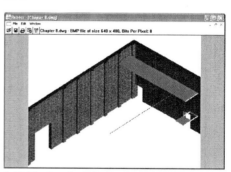

8-38 The Render Window.

Landscape Objects

A few standard objects are included in the AutoCAD Landscape Library which you will find useful. In Particular a rather scruffy man called People#2 (he looks a bit like a Production Manager) *Fig 8-40*.

Landscape Items are .tga files that are inserted to add a bit more realism to a rendered drawing and as well as couple of

8-39 File Output dialogue box.

8-40 Landscape Object 'People#2' Production Manager complete with bag of old schedules, budgets and sandwiches.

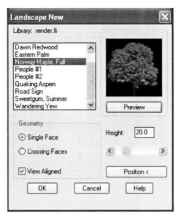

8-41 Landscape New dialogue box.

people a few bits of foliage are included. A Landscape item consists of two Images, the actual picture itself and an opacity mask, which allows the underlying rendered drawing to show through the gaps.

Click View ➤ Render ➤ Landscape New to open the dialogue box *Fig 8-41*

Select your object and preview it, then adjust the Height to 100. The height is in mm, so it is very small on an average stage. Next click Position and locate the Landscape object on the drawing. As you click you are returned to the dialogue box, click OK to return to the drawing.

The View Aligned button, selected by default, means that in any view you use the image will face you. Remember this is a purely decorative image, not a 3D object. Because of this it appears in the model as a triangle with a label *Fig 8-42*.

As mentioned before the image is very small, although actually its own full size. You may have trouble finding it! Once you have located it get the Grips on, select the top Grip and using Stretch make the object a sensible height. In the case of our Production Manager I used the following:

```
** STRETCH **
Specify stretch point or [Base
point/Copy/Undo/eXit]: @0,0,1700.
```

When you render the image you will see your figure which helps give scale to a design.

8-42 Landscape object as it appears prior to rendering. It may be resized using Grips.

Lights

Lights in AutoCAD are somewhat limited and therefore I do not recommend trying to light a show using them. Other programs such as WYSIWYG are much better at this as is LD Assistant®, an AutoCAD plug in.

These lights may be useful for a designer looking at a model who wants to create some more directional light and therefore give his model some more definition than the default ambience provided by AutoCAD. With a bit of work you may also be able to provide your lighting designer with a few hints!

To create a light:

Either Click View ➢ Render ➢ Light

or Click the Light Icon on the Render Toolbar

or Type light ⏎ at the Command Line.

This will open the Lights dialogue box *Fig 8-43*.

In the drop down box, select Spotlight then click New, which will open the New Spotlight dialogue box *Fig 8-44*.

Lights Icon (and part of Pixar's logo).

Firstly give your light a name: 1 will probably do. You can now also adjust the beam from the lamp, via the Hot Spot and Fall Off sliders. This is obviously useful if you have a particular lantern in mind. Leave the Attenuation as it is, despite it not being wholly appropriate for lanterns. Switch on Shadows to add a bit of atmosphere.

Next, if you wish you can play with the colour to give an approximation of gel colour. Use the Select Colour button to open the dialogue box. You can pick the approximate colour in the large box, and fine-tune it with the slider. This results in a number in the bottom box

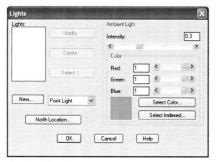

8-43 Lights dialogue box.

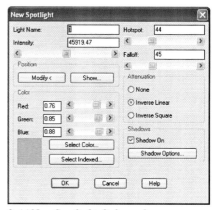

8-44 New Spotlight dialogue box .

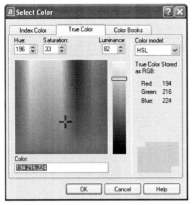

Fig 8-45. I found that 238,225,180 is an OK Straw, whilst 194,216,224 makes a respectable Light Steel Blue. Feel free to go mad with the colours but do remember to make a note of any ones you like and may want to use again. Click OK when you have your colour. You really need to see it once rendered to be able to judge the accuracy of your choice.

8-45 Lights Select Color dialogue box
The colour selected is a very
approximate Light Steel Blue.

Lastly, we need to position our light. Click the Modify button and watch the command line:

```
Enter light target
<current>:
```

This is where you want the centre of the beam to hit. I have selected an area of the back wall.

```
Enter light location <current>:
```

Pick a point on the flying bar we created earlier. In placing the light, you may find it easier if you have firstly inserted a lantern symbol onto the bar using the Blocks we set up earlier and then place the Light on the nose of this object. Obviously for Lighting Designers it is easier to have the Lantern symbol you are using and Light to share common photometric characteristics.

Now render the drawing, making sure you check the Shadows box and see what you have created. *Figs 8-46a-c* overleaf show renderings with different coloured spotlights.

There are two other kinds of Light. The Point Light creates the light from an ordinary light bulb, casting light in all directions from a set point, whilst a Distant Light has parallel beams like the Sun. This is probably the least useful to us, and most of the time, we will use a Spotlight, although Point Lights can be used to simulate candles. You will need to adjust the colour and turn the intensity down to a minimum of 2000 to create a candle glow.

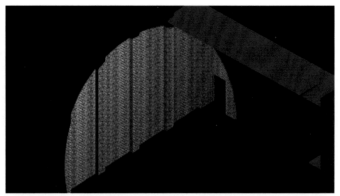

8-46a A section of the back wall Rendered with the spotlight coloured in Light Steel Blue.

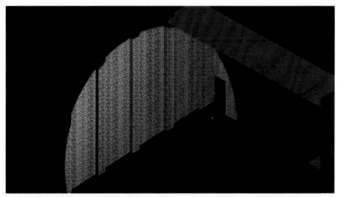

8-46b A section of the back wall Rendered with the spotlight coloured in Straw.

8-46c A section of the back wall Rendered with the spotlight coloured in Open White.

Exercise 11

Draw the figure *Fig Ex 11a*, as it is for you to practice these techniques I have not dimensioned it.

Some vital statistics to help you:

The Wall flat is
4880 x 6110 x 50

The Steps are
200 x 200 x 1000

The Ramp is
1000 x 2000 x 600

The balcony rail is made from cylinders of 25 radius, 900 high.

The windows and doors I will leave to you to decide, the same with any materials; I offer my effort only as an example *Fig Ex 11b*.

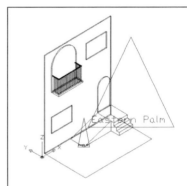

Ex 11a Unrendered version of my drawing. Use your own discretion for door and window size and design.

Add some lights and play with their colours. See what effect they have on the Landscape Objects.

Ex 11b Rendered version with added figure and palm tree. Again, use your own materials to suit your model.

3D Views

Although the standard Orthographic views are fine for most drawing and editing activities, there may be times that you want to view your model from a particular angle. An example would be from an extreme sightline for instance.

3D Orbit allows you to rotate the model in any axis, allowing you to choose a point of view from any angle. These views can then be saved for later repeated use.

Click View ➢ 3D Orbit and the Arcball appears around the drawing. If your cursor is outside the Arcball then the drawing will roll around an imaginary point in the centre of the screen and running in the Z axis towards you. If you are in this mode the cursor looks like a circular arrow. The orbit commands are operated by clicking and holding the left mouse button, then moving the mouse. Try this to see the effect *Fig 8-47*.

If you now place your cursor inside the Arcball it changes to a different type of icon – a sort of

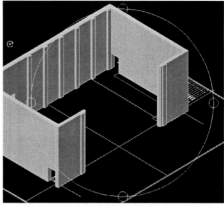

8-47 3D Orbit Showing the Arcball and the circular arrow 'roll' cursor.

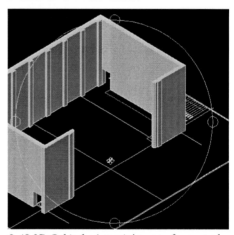

8-48 3D Orbit the 'atomic' cursor for control orbit around any axis within the Arcball.

atomic symbol possibly best describes it *Fig 8-48*. If you now left click, hold and move the mouse, then the model will start tumbling in whichever direction you send it. Running your mouse left-right will cause the model to roll that way, going up or down the screen and the model moves head over heels.

This can be very disorientating so right click and a sub menu will pop up. On this select More ➢ Orbit Maintains Z. This means when you move left or right the model rotates around the current Z axis. I emphasis current Z axis. As ever in 3D check that your UCS is correctly orientated for what you want to do.

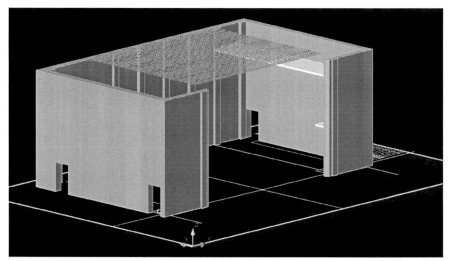

8-49 The theatre model in the standard Parallel projection.

Rotate your model until it looks something like *Fig 8-49*. Now right click again and this time pick Projection from the menu. At the moment we are using Parallel projection, select Perspective and your drawing will change appearance. The walls now recede to a vanishing point and hence the whole thing looks more realistic *Fig 8-50*. Perspective has its limitations however, for instance once you leave 3D orbit by opening the sub menu and click Exit,

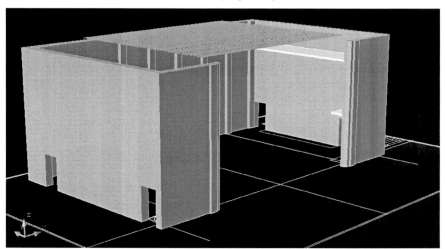

8-50 The model viewed from the same position but now in Perspective projection.

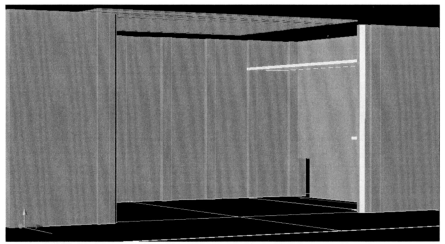

8-51 View from the rear stalls, again in Perspective.

you will not be able to use Zoom and Pan until you change the perspective view back to parallel. Therefore you should only change the projection when you have everything finished and you are about to render this view.

Use the 3D orbit to move the model around until you are looking across the stage from the back of the stalls. Use Zoom to move in and approximate a seat position then switch the projection to Perspective. You should have something like *Fig 8-51*.

Now that you have your point of view, click View ➤ Named Views which will open the View dialogue box *Fig 8-52*. Click New, give your view a name then click OK.

You can create as many views as are required for the project. You may want to align some of them with your venue's sightlines to check the extremes or as we have just done random seats in the house. These can then be rendered and used to present your design concepts or just check the look of something prior to design and production meetings. If you have a 3D template then these are part of that drawing in the same way as the other aids we have created.

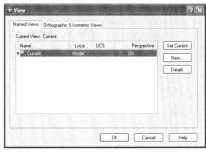

8-52 View dialogue box, Named Views tab. Any Views created are saved here.

Exercise 12

Complete as much as you can of the rest of the theatre. An example is shown in *Fig Ex 12.*

This can be an ongoing project, add as much or as little detail as you require. Ultimately you should try this with your own theatre. The model shown here is of the RSAMD's New Athenaeum Theatre in Glasgow *Fig Ex 12a.*

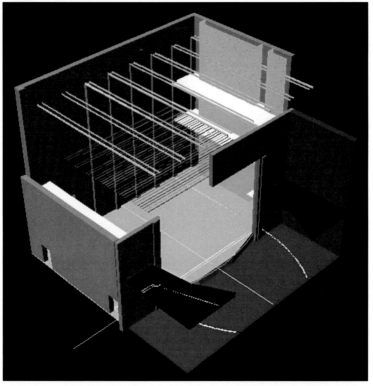

A more advanced version of the Theatre model. Some FOH features have been added as has a loading Gallery, all the Flying Bars and Grid Beams. The covers for the Counterweights have also been added using a mesh Hatch, making them transparent.

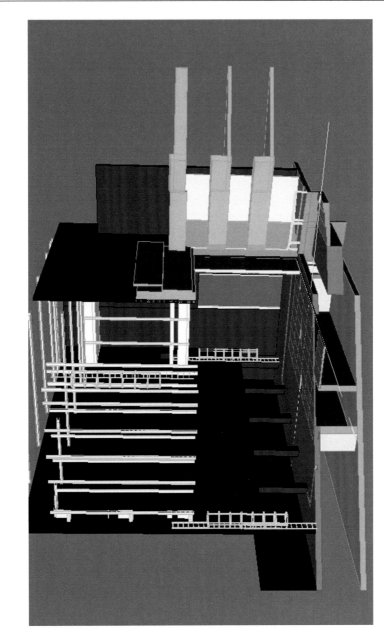

Ex 12 RSAMD – New Athenaeum Theatre. Some of the walls have been cut away using the techniques demonstrated in this chapter to create a sectional view.

CHAPTER TIPS

Tip!

Moving the UCS can be quite daunting but in the majority of cases there is an easy way to do so. The way outlined earlier in the chapter requires a fair bit of thought so if possible try to use the options below first.

Firstly, create a simple box, then switch to an isometric view.

Now type UCS followed by n for New. There is now a range of options for relocating the UCS. We will have a look at a few of them.

B8-1 UCS moved using 3Point – the arrows indicate the picks.

3Point is nice and easy to use if you have square faces. Type 3P and then pick firstly the origin (where X and Y cross) then a point on the X axis then the Y axis, the command line looks like this:

```
Specify new origin point
<0,0,0>:
Specify point on positive
portion of X-axis
Specify point on positive-Y
portion of the UCS XY plane
```

Your UCS will move as shown in *Fig B8 -1.*

Object Uses a part of the wireframe to position the UCS. Clicking on any wireframe causes that line to become the X axis. The Origin will be placed as near as possible to the next intersection. This means that one line has two possible orientations. Type ob and then just pick the wireframe line *Fig B8-2.*

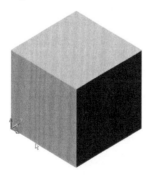

B8-2 UCS Moved using Object – the Arrows shows the part of the cube picked.

Face Aligns the UCS with a face of the solid. Again the choice of where you pick on the face influences the orientation of the UCS *Fig B8-3*

View This is a useful tool for adding Text to a view as it aligns the UCS with the computer screen *Fig B8-4.*

If any of these Views are reusable in a drawing save them for later as shown earlier.

You should always be aware of the orientation of the UCS when using the 3D preset views. Sometimes the UCS will be in a completely different orientation. This seems to occur particularly when changing from a 'section' type view such as Left or Front to an isometric view. If this

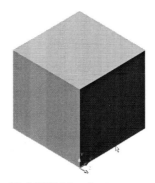

B8-3 UCS Moved using Face.

happens you will find objects behaving most unexpectedly as the xes are not at all in the relationship you assume them to be in. *Figs B8-5 a,b &c*

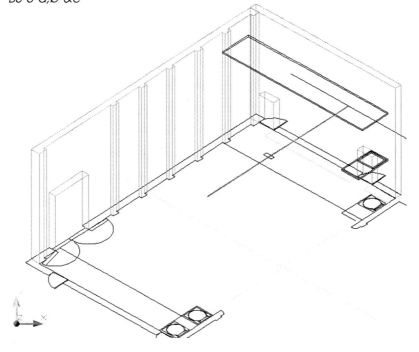

B8-4 UCS in the View position – aligned with the screen.

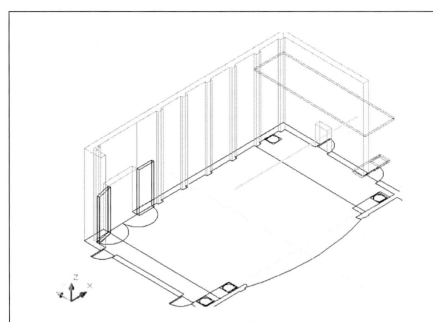

B8-5a SW Isometric view. UCS is in fact the WCS.

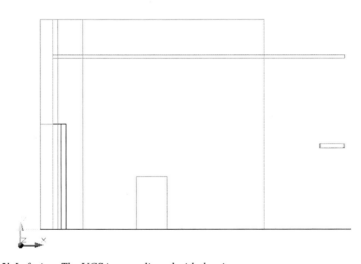

B8-5b Left view. The UCS is now aligned with the view.

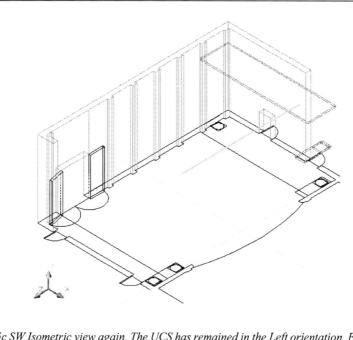

B8-5c SW Isometric view again. The UCS has remained in the Left orientation. Editing or drawing without changing this will give unexpected results!

9 PLOTTING YOUR DRAWINGS

We have worked exclusively in the electronic medium until now. However in order to communicate the information on our model to those in workshops, onstage and in the rehearsal room at some point we will need to produce hard copy. This is something (a piece of paper) that can be referred to without specialist equipment. Although PDAs such as Palms are much more prevalent they have yet to replace a printed drawing and until they do you will need to know how to reproduce your drawings.

Plotting a drawing in AutoCAD is very simple; plotting a drawing to a certain scale less so and plotting multiple views to different scales a bit more complex. Let's start with the basics. Printing a drawing is generally referred to as Plotting in CAD systems, plotters are generally large format (A2 and above) printers producing either colour or black and white plots. According to the specifications of a machine, they can cost many thousands of pounds to buy.

Basic Plotting

We will look firstly at plotting onto our local printer – just to go through the process and look at the various options. Use your theatre model and make sure it is in plan view with any shading or rendering off.

Either Click File ➢ Plot

or Click the Plot Icon on the Standard Toolbar.

This will open up the Plot dialogue box, which has two tabs *Fig 9-1.*

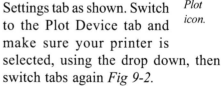

9-1 Plot dialogue box – Plot Settings tab.

If it has opened on the Plot *The* Settings tab as shown. Switch *Plot* to the Plot Device tab and *icon.* make sure your printer is selected, using the drop down, then switch tabs again *Fig 9-2.*

The plot settings tab has a variety of options: we will start with Paper Size and Paper Units. Assuming you have a normal size home printer you will

9-2 Plot dialogue box – Plot Device tab.

9-3 Scales differ according to the radio button selected, in this case Display = 1:136.3.

9-4 Extents = 1:116.1.

9-5 Limits = 1: 106.8.

probably need to change the paper size to A4 via the drop down box. Once you have done this then the display will show you the area of your sheet that can be used to print on. This size takes account of any mechanism required to pass the paper through the printer or plotter and so is less than the actual paper size.

As we have been using metric units throughout make sure the millimetre radio button is selected, as soon as you do this then in the Plot Scale area a scale will appear. This scale has many options: the default is Scaled to Fit so you will start with a rather odd scale, in the illustration it is 1:136.3. Whilst Scaled to Fit is selected, the scale is also dependant on the selection in the Plot Area to the left. As you can see, choosing a different radio button alters the scale *Figs 9-3 to 9-5.*

The options are as follows:

Limits   All of the drawing will be plotted out to the Limits you made when first setting the drawing up.

Extents   The plot will fit around everything drawn regardless of the Limits.

Display   Whatever is currently showing in the Drawing Area will be plotted.

View   If you have created any Views, usually in 3D work, then you can select a View to plot.

Window   By clicking the button you can select an area to be plotted.

If you want to plot at a particular scale, then by using the drop down, you can pick from the many metric and imperial options. Unfortunately 1:25 is not considered a standard scale.

Leave it at Scaled to Fit and click the Partial Preview button. This gives a simple indication as to whether your drawing will fit onto the page at this scale *Fig 9-6*. Click OK to return to the Plot dialogue box then Click Full Preview.

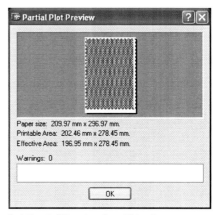

Full Preview shows you the drawing as a sheet of paper and this is how it will be plotted. A Full Preview should be done each time prior to the actual plot just to make sure *Fig 9-7*. The command line reads:

```
Press ESC or ENTER to
exit, or right-click
to display shortcut
menu.
```

9-6 Partial Preview box This gives a general indication as to whether the drawing will fit on the paper.

Right click to open the submenu and select Exit. In the Plot dialogue box, if your drawing looks like figure 9-7 then check the Center the plot box in the Plot Offset area and preview again *Fig 9-8*.

Lastly, in the Plot Options area uncheck Plot with plot styles. By default Plot object lineweights becomes active. Preview again to check the appearance of the Lineweights on the drawing. Remember the Lineweight settings are real world thicknesses we have assigned to certain Layers. In some cases they may appear out of proportion to the rest of the drawing.

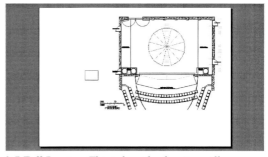

9-7 Full Preview. This is how the drawing will appear when plotted.

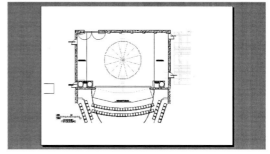

9-8 The drawing has now been centred up on the page.

If you are happy with everything you can now click OK, or if you are in Preview right click then Plot and your drawing will print.

Plotting to Scale

Now while using this method is handy to quickly check things, the main point of accurate drawing by any system is to produce scaled drawings. When we first set up the Theatre drawing, we used a sheet of A0 as a basis for our Limits and multiplied the sheet size by 25. It therefore follows that to create our 1:25 scale drawing we need to plot on a machine capable of handling A0 size paper.

We need to add a plotter on our system so that we can set up and preview this drawing. We don't actually need a plotter to be connected (unless you have one) as many of us will be taking the drawing to a reprographic company to be produced. In this case, you would need to know their plotter model.

Click Tools ➤ Wizards ➤ Add Plotter. The wizard will open. Follow the screenshots below to set up an example A0 plotter *Figs 9-9 to 9-16.*

9-9 Add Plotter – Introduction Page.

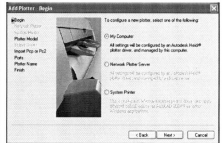

9-10 Add Plotter - Begin.

9-11 Add Plotter – Plotter Model. Choose the device indicated (DesignJet 650C C2859B).

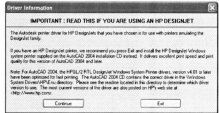

9-12 Add Plotter – HP Warning, click Continue.

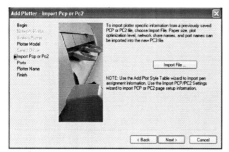

9-13 Add Plotter – Import file, click Next.

9-14 Add Plotter – Ports, select any spare Port and click Next.

9-15 Add Plotter – Plotter Name. Anything you can use to identify the plotter can be used here.

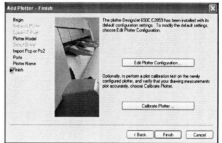

9-16 Add Plotter - Finish.

Layouts

Until now, we have been working in what is known as Model Space: in Model Space, we draw our objects at full size.

Paper Space is the best place to arrange our drawing to be plotted out at a given scale. We can set up various plots at given scales for paper sizes using Paper Space and in particular the Layout system. In Paper Space we draw objects at the size they will appear when plotted out.

Now that we have a Plotter capable of taking our drawing, we need to create a Layout. Layouts are the tabs that are at the bottom of the drawing area. When creating our drawings we have worked on the Model tab and as you can see there are also two Layout tabs that are created by default. Click on either of them to open it. You will see your drawing on a sheet of paper. The border we drew earlier is shown, as is a dashed border. The dashed border indicates the extent of plotting space available on this sheet of paper

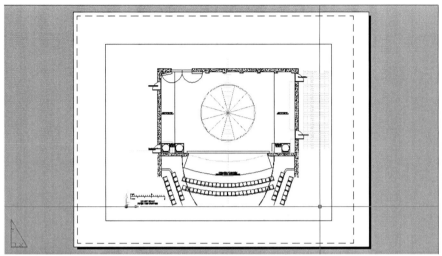

9-17 One of the default Layouts created as part of any new drawing.

for this particular printer (generally AutoCAD will detect your Windows printer, or sometimes None) *Fig 9-17.*

You can set up several Layouts, each one at a different scale for a different paper size. This means you will not have to keep changing the Plot parameters (as we did earlier) each time you want to produce a drawing at a different scale.

Prior to this doing this we will set up a couple of Layers that we will use specifically for plotting. We previously inserted the Title Box for our drawing on the Layer 9a General Notes – Title Block. Create a copy of this layer with the same attributes, except the name is 9a PS General Notes – Title Block. Secondly, our drawing border is on Layer 0 but we do not need it for plotting. We do however need a border in Paper Space so create Layer 0 PS Border. Make sure this layer is current before starting the next section.

9-18 Create Layout – Begin dialogue. Here you can name your layout so make it as informative as possible..

Now click Tools ➤ Wizards ➤ Create Layout and the wizard will open with the Begin Screen

Fig 9-18. Enter 1-25@A0 as the name and click Next. Pick the Hewlett Packard DesignJet 650C 2859B plotter from the list and click next.

Choose ISO expand A0 from the drop down box in the next screen *Fig 9-19* and click next then click through the next two screens, Orientation and Title Block, accepting the defaults. You can do the same with the Define Viewports and Pick Location dialogues also. Finally click Finish and you will be taken into the Layout where you can see your drawing on a sheet of paper, just like the full preview screen *Fig 9-20.* The UCS has also changed to the Paper Space version although a Model Space UCS may still

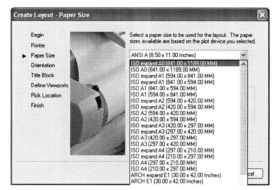

9-19 Create Layout – Paper Size showing some of the sizes available to this particular plotter.

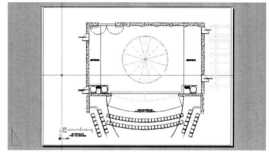

9-20 The new Layout, note we are in Paper Space, the UCS has changed and the cross hairs cover the whole screen.

also be present inside the Viewport – *Fig 9-21.* On the Status bar the button marked Model has changed to Paper also indicating that we have moved outside Model Space.

You will see another border outside our current one. This is the edge of our Viewport; everything inside it will be plotted and is at its plotted size. The first job is to turn off the Layer 0 border (if you haven't already done so). Then click on the Paper Space border so the Grips appear. Now open up the Properties Pallete. Under Misc, the Standard Scale actually reads Custom. As with the Plot box there are a lot of other scales accessible via the drop down –

SNAP GRID ORTHO POLAR OSNAP OTRACK LWT PAPER

9-21 The Status Bar showing also that we are in Paper Space.

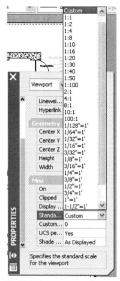

9-22 The range of Standard scales available from the Properties palette. Of course 1: 25 is not one of them.

unfortunately 1-25 is not one of them *Fig 9-22*. The calculation required to find our scale factor is as follows:

100 ÷ Target Scale ÷ 100

So in this case that is $100 ÷ 25 = 4; 4 ÷ 100 = 0.04$.

Enter this number into the Custom Scale box and the layout will change to the new scale.

Exit the Properties Palette and double click inside the drawings border. You are now back in Model Space and the crosshairs are restricted to the viewport.

To highlight the difference in scale between the two let us type some text in Model Space and then in Paper Space. Using either of our set fonts type Model Space anywhere in the drawing. The size is set as either 100 for Minor Text or 200 for Major Text, depending on which one you use. Because of the size of our stage area the text is quite small.

Swap to Paper Space by clicking outside the border and repeat the Text command, typing Paper Space this time. The text will be huge as Paper Space is the size of a real piece of paper so if you type something that is 200mm tall it takes up a lot of space *Fig 9-23*.

Remember when we set up our text styles we aimed to have them at certain sizes when plotted? In Model Space they are 100 and 200mm high. Minor text is 4mm and Major Text 8mm high in Paper Space. If you need to make notes on the plotted page then set up two more Text Styles just for Paper Space with the fonts set to the appropriate size.

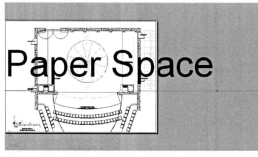

9-23 Text in Paper Space: unfortunately the text size here is set in Model Space (200mm).

Now we will insert a new Title Box to replace the old one. The current one will remain and is a useful reference to any one using the model. However some parts of the Title Box may be different when plotted and other Layouts are created, in particular the Scale. Switch off the Layer for the current

Title Box and make the PS one active. By adding a new Title Box in the Layout we don't have to edit our usual one and then remember to change it again. We do however have to scale it when inserting into Paper Space otherwise the Title Block will be several times larger than the drawing *Fig* 9-24. The scale required will be the same as the overall scale we set earlier in the Properties Palette. The Title Block inserted into this Layout is unique and can only be edited from here so there is little chance of wrong scale information being plotted as there can be when plotting different scales directly from Model Space.

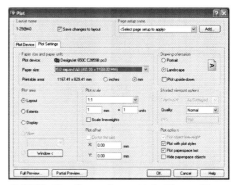

9-24 Model Space Title Block inserted into Paper Space. The Block should be scaled at 0.04, the scale required to make the drawing 1:25 on an A0 sheet.

Once you are satisfied your drawing is at it should be you can start the Plot sequence as before. The dialogue box does look slightly different *Fig 9-25*.

Firstly things like the Plotter model and paper size are already selected, next in the Plot Area section, Layout is selected and finally the Scale is set at 1-1. Remember we are dealing with a piece of paper here, so this is correct.

Preview your drawing as usual and if everything is OK, you are ready to Plot, which you can do from the sub menu by right clicking as before.

Having a Layout set up for each scale, paper size and plotter that you regularly use saves you a lot of time as well as having to fiddle about with the actual model and then remembering to amend any details each time you change scale, etc.

You may find that upon creating a Layout the page looks like it did in *Fig 9-17*.

The outer dashed line represents the maximum plot area available. If your border is inside, then activate

9-25 Plotting from a Layout tab. Many of the parameters are set during the creation of the layout.

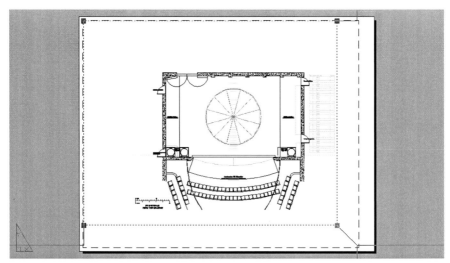

9-26 A Basic Layout – the dashed line indicates the maximum plot size. The Viewport is resized using Grips.

the Grips and drag them out to the dashed line *Fig 9-26*. Once the drawing's Viewport is as large as possible then scale as required. It is important to remember that when you are in a Layout, selecting a Viewport and then zooming will affect the scale within that Viewport. This is where the analogy of a Viewport being a shape cut out of a piece of paper through which you can see your model comes in handy.

Imagine you are standing at the back of the auditorium holding a piece of A0 paper with the Viewport cut out. Looking through the hole you will see most of the stage, the prosc and some of the auditorium. If you now move closer to the stage then details on the prosc become larger; in effect they are a bigger scale. For this reason you should always set scales via the Property Palette and then leave them. If you need to zoom in and change something, do it in the Model tab where it will be updated in all your layouts. It is also impossible to set an accurate scale via the zoom wheel.

Ex 13

Create the following Layouts using the same plotter as above.

Paper size   Scale

A2   1:50
A3   1:75
A4   1:100

Give each Layout its own Title Box, with the correct information on it, and plot those your printer can handle.

Using an Outside Plotter

Sometimes, for a variety of reasons, we may not have access to a printer that can handle large scale drawings. They are very expensive and take up a lot of room after all. However, there are many professional print houses that can handle our plotting.

Before going to them there are a couple of things to consider. Firstly there is the problem of the staff's familiarity with AutoCAD. It may be something that they use rarely and this can cause problems with correct scaling and appearance of the drawing.

As an example, I have been the victim of a company who could not figure out how to plot from an A0 Layout I had set up for them. Instead of calling me and asking, they did manage to print an A3 version. They then enlarged this on a photocopier until it did fit onto a sheet of A0. Needless to say, this was nowhere near the correct scale of 1:25 and caused a lot of confusion at the mark up, not to mention wasted time.

The second question allied with the first is that of security of your drawing. Are you happy to hand your design in an open file to a print shop, and, more importantly, are you sure they know how to handle a .dwg file? They may inadvertently change your drawing again, causing you several headaches later on.

As a result, many companies recommend you save your AutoCAD files as an HPGL2.plt Plot files. A .plt file embeds all the information in a drawing, which means it can't be accidentally edited. By saving as a .plt it also means any image files such as logos are also included, saving the whole hassle of having to include them on a disk for plotting.

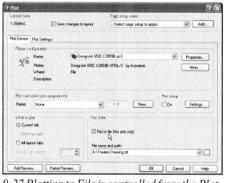

A Plot file is created from the Plot dialogue box. Use a Layout as before and preview the drawing. Once you are satisfied that it is correct, click on the Plot Device tab and check Plot to file *Fig 9-27*.

A file name and location will be suggested, but you can also pick your own location using the browse button. Usually you will be saving it to a floppy or ZIP disc. Some repro shops will also deal with plotting via

9-27 Plotting to File is controlled from the Plot Device tab.

email (you still have to go and get the print though). Once this is done, simply click OK to save the drawing as a file.

If the plotter is colour but you want a (cheaper) black and white plot then on this tab in the Plot Style Table (pen assignments) – Name drop down, select monochrome.ctb. This will make sure it is B&W. If you want any colours shaded use one of the Greyscale options. Preview will show you exactly what the plot will look like.

Plot Stamps

Whilst we are here there is also the option of putting a Plot Stamp on your drawing. This is a simple line of text that can be placed on the plotted drawing. It can be anything you want, the file location, a version number, or any other information or warnings required.

By checking On, then clicking Settings, the Plot Stamp dialogue box opens *Fig 9-28*. There are default

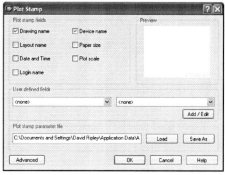

9-28 Plot Stamp settings dialogue box.

buttons for what will be included in the stamp but you can also create your own stamp by clicking on the Add/Edit button.

Clicking Advanced opens up options such as the location of the Plot Stamp and the font style and size. The size of the font is in Paper Space units so be aware of the size you set this to. Unfortunately if you are previewing the drawing the Plot Stamp will not be shown. The Preview box in the dialogue box only gives an indication of the location.

For those of you using an Educational version of AutoCAD there is an additional Plot Stamp automatically produced which you cannot get rid of, although in my experience its implementation is a bit hit and miss *Fig 9-29*.

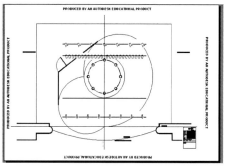

9-29 Plot Stamp included in the Educational version of AutoCAD. For obvious reasons this cannot be removed.

Plotting Multiple Viewports

As we saw when drawing in 3D, having more than one Viewport open can be advantageous. This also applies when plotting a 3D object. There are two methods of doing this: both involve creating a new Layout. Open up your Theatre drawing and make sure the 3D Layers are all on.

Now start the Layout Wizard: use your plotter and accept the defaults by clicking next until you get to the Define Viewports box. This time check Std 3D Engineering Views and complete the creation of the Layout. This Layout has 4 Viewports, clockwise from the top left, Plan (Top), Isometric, Right and Front *Fig 9-30.*

You can change these Views by clicking inside the Viewport and changing as you would in the model if these aren't right for your purpose. You can also select the kind of view offered in each Viewport. For example, you can have the Isometric rendered, Front hidden and everything else as simple wireframes *Fig 9-31.*

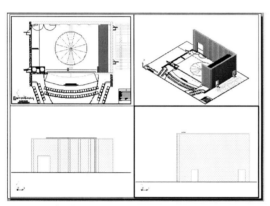

9-30 Standard Engineering Viewport configuration.

You can also select which layers are visible in each view port by using the Freeze or Thaw in Current Viewport option in the Layer Manager.

Make sure you are in Model Space in the relevant Viewport then using the drop down Freeze a Layer. The Layer will disappear from the current Viewport but still be shown in all the others.

Layer Manager icon

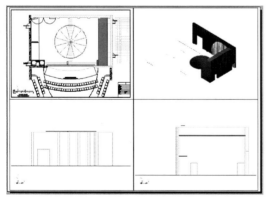

9-31 Standard Engineering Viewports with changed View properties in each Viewport.

You can also create your own Viewports without using

the standard options in the Layout Wizard.

Create a new Layout, accepting all the defaults, when your layout appears, click on the border to activate the Grips. Pick either of the bottom Grips and move them to halfway up the page, use the Midpoint osnap *Fig 9-32*.

Now click Views ➤ Viewports ➤ 2 Viewports. The command line will read

```
Command:  _-
vports
```

Specify corner of viewport or

```
[ON/OFF/Fit/Shadeplot/Lock/Object/Polygonal/
Restore/2/3/4] <Fit>: _2
Enter viewport arrangement [Horizontal/
Vertical] <Vertical>:
```

Accept the default by pressing Enter

```
Specify first corner or [Fit] <Fit>:
```

Pick the bottom left corner of the top Viewport.

```
Specify opposite
corner:
```

Pick the bottom right corner of the dashed border

```
Regenerating
model.
```

Your drawing should now look like *Fig 9-33*. You will need to resize and pan in the top Viewport to make it fit better.

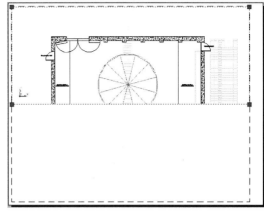

9-32 Creating your own Viewports. The Main Viewport has been reduced in size using the Grips. This leaves room for other Viewports to be added.

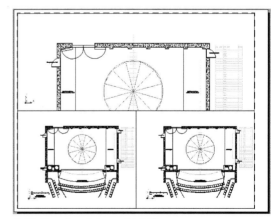

9-33 Completed sheet with 3 Viewports.

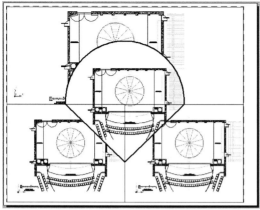

9-34 The same sheet with a Polygonal Viewport also added.

size you will plot to, not the model size.

You can also create a Viewport that is not rectangular. Click Views ➢ Viewports ➢ Polygonal Viewport

Select a start point and now using Lines and Arcs via the command line options, you can create a Viewport of any shape *Fig 9-34*. Remember that Viewports in Layouts are in paper Space, therefore the co ordinates you may be inputting to create the Viewports refer to the sheet

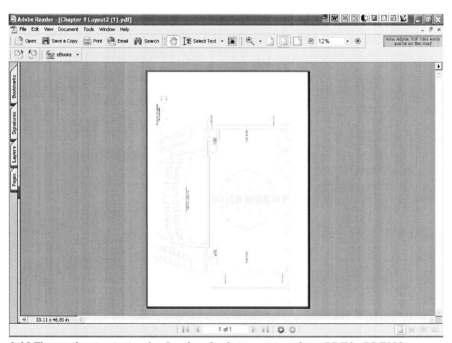

9-35 Theatre drawing in Acrobat Reader after being converted to a PDF by PDF995.

Creating a Portable Document Format (PDF) File

You will often be dealing with people who do not have access to AutoCAD. You may also be sending to people who have AutoCAD and need a drawing, which you would rather they didn't have the ability to alter.

Creating a PDF file is one solution although there are also others, as we shall see in the next chapter. The reason this is included here is that a program capable of creating PDFs acts as a virtual plotter. Adobe Acrobat® is the obvious choice for this function but there are free PDF creators such as PDF995®, which can also be used.

You can create a Layout just for PDF creation. The PDF program will appear in the list of available plotters. You can create the PDF as you would an A0 plotter so that if your recipient wants to print the drawing they can do so at the correct scale.

Once the Layout is set up, it works just as any other with the difference being that you will be asked for a location to save your PDF to, as with plotting to file. Depending on what your software is you will probably see a screen showing progress of the PDF creation. When this has finished, a program, such as Adobe's free Acrobat Reader or any other PDF reader, may open and display the newly created file *Fig 9-35.*

Exercise 14

Create the following:

A four way view port with a Polygonal central Viewport.
What each view is up to you. *Fig Ex 14* is an example

Once you have done that, create Layouts for the drawing that will
produce:

A HPGL2 .plt file

A PDF file

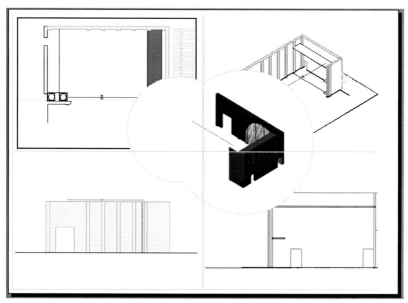

Ex 14 Target drawing for Ex 14.

10 EXCHANGING DRAWINGS WITH OTHER PROGRAMS

AutoCAD as you may have noticed, is not the only CAD program you can get, although it is the most popular in terms of sales. Many other CAD programs are available as well as specialist programs, particularly in the lighting field. In this, the final chapter, we will look at sending AutoCAD programs to other applications.

Firstly a word about the file format used by AutoCAD: .dwg. This is a proprietary format owned by Autodesk. As a result, the code is not publicly available and with every few releases, the format changes slightly but significantly in terms of older versions of AutoCAD and other programs. For instance, although AutoCAD 2004 will open .dwg files from AutoCAD R14 and 2000, the reverse is not true. You cannot open a newer version of AutoCAD in R14 or 2000. The 2000 release .dwg format also covers 2000i and 2002.

Because of this and the domination of .dwg as the main drawing file format, other companies find it difficult to keep their releases compatible with the current AutoCAD version. The Open Design Alliance is a group of companies who in crude terms reverse engineer the current Autodesk .dwg format then release it to the publishers of rival programs. The format they produce is known as OpenDWG. Naturally this is sometimes less successful than hoped but until Autodesk release the code it is the only way forward for many CAD programs. Most of the producers of the software listed below are members of the Open Design Alliance.

DXF

The common format that is freely available for everyone to use is .dxf Drawing Exchange File format. One problem with .dxf is that file sizes are much larger than .dwg and again the format has changed with different releases so you must ensure compatibility with your target application. There are also limitations as to what is actually translated as well as keeping both .dwg and dxf versions of a file up to date.
The DXF file Icon

To create a .dxf file just Click File ➢ Save as, then pick the correct version of .dxf from the drop down. As you can see there are three types AutoCAD

2004, AutoCAD 2000 and R12, which will also work for R14 *Fig 10-1*.

When opening a .dxf you will again have to select the file type, as .dwg is the default. You should not notice any differences between a .dwg and .dxf file but this may sometimes occur, depending on how different programs handle the files.

DWF

The Design Web Format file is a way of sending drawings to those

10-1 Creating a DXF file using Save As and selecting the File Type.

without AutoCAD. The drawings can then be viewed in a viewer and plotted from there. The Autodesk Express Viewer is bundled with AutoCAD, but the Autodesk DWF Viewer, which can be downloaded from the Autodesk Website, has replaced it.

If you need to mark up a drawing and return it to the originator in the DWF format then the Autodesk DWF Composer is needed which allows notations to be made, and measurements taken. Both versions, Viewer and Composer, can print your drawing to scale. An original .dwg can be converted to DWF in Composer, so that it can be worked on without affecting the original file.

Let us create a DWF from our Theatre Model. We will create a plan for others to look at so switch off any 3D layers you may have on at the moment. Create a Layout that is for an A0 plot @ 1:25 as we have done previously.

Either Click File ➤ Publish

or Click the Publish Icon on the Standard toolbar

This will open the Publish Drawing Sheets Dialogue *Fig 10-2*. *The* You may get a warning box asking about saving changes. If you do, *DWF* just click OK to proceed. *Publish*

In the dialogue box there is a large pane on the left in which are *Icon* listed all the tabs that are available to be published, including the Model tab and any layouts. Highlight the model tab and click remove it using the button on the right side of the box. Next in the box below the list of drawing sheets choose a location to save the file to. Below that is the option to password protect the file. Add a password if you want here. They are case sensitive so be aware of this when passing them on later.

Once you have done this, click the large Publish button. A confirm Password dialogue box opens, so re-enter the password *Fig10-3*. A Now Plotting dialogue briefly opens, followed by the Plot Progress dialogue box we have seen before: yes, DWF also uses a Plotter emulator to create the file.

10-2 Publish Sheets dialogue box. From this window you can select what parts of your drawing to publish.

When the virtual plot is complete then a new dialogue box opens. In this case, I am going to have a look at the DWF file and make some notes on it using DWF Composer.

To do this, click View DWF File. If you don't have DWF Composer, DWF Viewer will open, but you cannot add any notes. As either program opens you will again have to input your password to continue.

10-3 Password protection is available when creating DWF as an added security measure.

Once opened, The program has navigation to the left and the drawing to the right *Fig 10-4*. Composer has a toolbar for annotation, which is lacking in Viewer *Fig 10-5*.

The toolbars icons are from left to right:

Selector is used to edit Mark Up objects after they are created.

Text Tool for inserting text.

Mark Up Tools use the drop down to access a range of

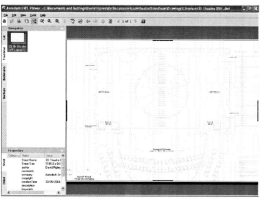

10-4 The selected drawing opened in DWF Viewer.

10-5 The DWF Composer Toolbar.

10-6 DWF Viewer/Composer Print dialogue box.

leaders and revision clouds.

Shape Tools again via the drop down a variety of lines, shapes and freehand drawing tools are available.

Stamp Tools a variety of pre-defined stamps such as Rejected, Not to Scale, etc.

Dimension Lines, Polylines and areas can be measured.

The final area of the toolbar deals with the size and appearance of any Text inserted.

Feel free to add any notes and stamps and then click File ➢ Print to open the Print dialogue box *Fig 10-6*.

In the Paper Size and Orientation section, pick A4 paper in landscape, and then check in the Reduce/Enlarge Drawing area that Print to Scale is at 100% and Tile Drawing is also selected. Then click Show

The DWF file Icon

Page Tiles. In the main drawing window, blue dashed lines will appear to show the A4 pages required to print the whole A0 drawing *Fig 10-7*.

As the Autodesk DWF Viewer is a free download, DWF is a useful and secure way of distributing drawings safe in the knowledge that the original model cannot be altered.

Exporting Raster Files

You can easily create a raster image of any drawing to BMP, JPG, PNG or TIFF

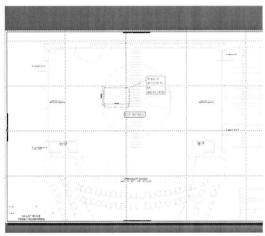

10-7 A0 drawing ready to print on an A4 printer. Annotation has been added in DWF Composer. The blue dashed lines show how the drawing will be split across several sheets of A4. This is known as tiling.

formats. This is done via the command line.

Type Either bmpout, jpgout, pngout or tifout ⏎ depending on the format you require. A standard save dialogue box entitled Create Raster File will open, with the format selected in the File Type box *Fig 10-8*. Name your file and click on Save. You will return to the drawing screen with a pick box cursor. The command line reads:

```
Select objects or
<all objects and
viewports>:
```

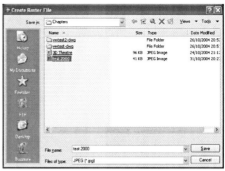

10-8 Create Raster File dialogue box. Depending on which file format you use the File Type will be set accordingly.

Right click to save the whole drawing or use the pick box to select the items you want to show. You can window using the pick box to select the parts of the drawing you want *Fig 10-9*. The background colour will always be exported regardless of how you pick the objects to be rasterised. Right click when you have chosen what is to be included. You will need to navigate to wherever you saved the file to view it in your graphics program *Fig 10-10*.

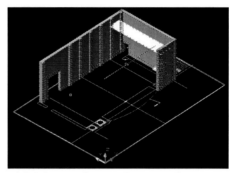

10-9 Selecting objects to be exported as a Raster File.

If you want to create a raster image of a Rendered drawing this is done via the Render window as detailed in Chapter 8.

Opening AutoCAD .dwgs in other programs

As we have noted above although

10-10 Raster File opened in PaintShop Pro. As you can see the background colour has been brought into the file although not actually selected.

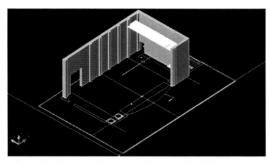

10-11 Test drawing for exporting to other CAD programs. Three versions were created: AutoCAD 2000, 2004 and a DXF file.

AutoCAD is the world's most used CAD program, many others are available. What follows is a brief survey of some CAD and other programs and methods of importing a .dwg into them. In each case, I will indicate which version of .dwg or .dxf I have used and the version of the target program. I have tried to use the most up-to-date versions available. The drawing has been saved as test 2000.dwg (2000 format) test 2004.dwg (2004 format) and test.dxf *Fig 10-11.*

The drawing I have used is based on our Theatre drawing. This has many Layers in it as well as 3D Solids. I have also added a couple of Dimensions in and there are already Blocks present.

In many cases, trial versions are available from the manufacturers' websites (their the addresses are shown in the bibliography).

I then opened a file native to the program. There are usually sample files included. I exported it via the DWG/DXF export routine and opened it in AutoCAD.

TurboCAD V10

This is the current version of TurboCAD, which is a popular and cheaper alternative to AutoCAD. The methodology behind creating drawings in TurboCAD is different from AutoCAD and so users can find switching from one to another a bit confusing. In fact, regardless of how disciplined you are, if you do swap between CAD programs you will find

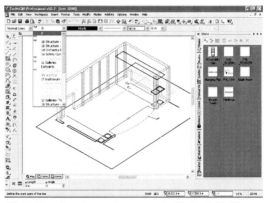

10-12 Test drawing as it appears in TurboCAD 10.

yourself issuing commands for one program whilst in another.

The test 2000 drawing opened as a DWG – Native AutoCAD Format file via the normal Open dialogue box. As you can see from the screen shot *Fig 10-12* this was a nice clean import, with everything as it should be including Blocks and dimensions.

The same was true of the test 2004 drawing; neither file would open however in TurboCAD 9.

10-13 TurboCAD Pavilion sample drawing as it appears in its native format.

I then opened a Sample drawing, Pavilion from the 3D samples folder. I then saved it as a dwg *Fig 10-13*. In TurboCAD this is done through File ➤ Save As and picking DWG _ AutoCAD Native File, but the AutoCAD version is not indicated.

The drawing opened with no problem in AutoCAD but with a slight change in appearance. The seats, which appear solid in the TurboCAD hidden drawing, have lost their tops in AutoCAD *Fig 10-14*.

VectorWorks V10.5

VectorWorks has several versions for different industries and is also available for use on the Mac. As well as the basic VectorWorks program there is a theatre lighting plug-in, Spotlight, which when used with RenderWorks is capable of providing photo realistic images. Spotlight can also generate all the usual paperwork information required for a lighting rig.

Neither dwg would work with VectorWorks 10.5 so I went down the dxf route. When the DXF DWG Import Options dialogue is shown it is important, in the 2D/3D

10-14 The Pavilion drawing in AutoCAD. Note how the bench and table tops have disappeared.

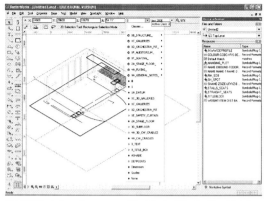

10-15 Test drawing opened in VectorWorks Spotlight.

Conversion area, to select All 3D from the drop down (the default is 2D and 3D). If you don't then when you select an Isometric view the 3D objects will move but the 2D parts will stay in Plan view, which looks a little odd. On the Objects tab, check Convert Dimensions to Groups – otherwise these will also stay on the same plane regardless of view.

Accept the default in the next dialogue box and the drawing will open to a Plan view. I changed the view to Left Isometric, via View ➤ Standard Views, which is the equivalent to AutoCAD's SW Isometric view. The result is shown in *Fig 10-15*.

VectorWorks has a system of Classes, which split down some of the Layers as shown in the illustration. Although they seem similar to Layers, they are actually very different in concept. All of our Blocks and dimensions have become Resources and are available via the right hand pane.

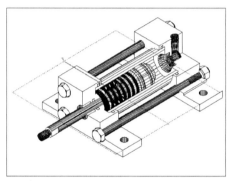

10-16 Air Cylinder drawing in VectorWorks.

I chose the Air Cylinder example from the limited number of sample drawings *Fig 10-16*. Conversion to dwg is via File ➤ Export ➤ Export DXF/DWG. DWG has to be selected from the drop down, as dxf is the default. All versions of

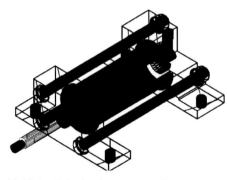

10-17 Air Cylinder drawing as it first appears when opened as a .dwg in AutoCAD.

AutoCAD back to R2.5 are catered for via another drop down.

When opening the file in AutoCAD, you will find that by saving the file as a .dwg you also created a folder which holds the drawing file, in this case Air Cylinder_dwg. When the drawing first opened it looked like huge LineWeights had been applied *Fig 10-17*. I then applied Hide to it and after regenerating, which took about two minutes, the drawing looked as it did in VectorWorks.

VectorWorks files tend to be quite large and the VectorWorks drawing is 3.3Mbwhilst the dwg version was 7.1Mb. As a comparison, the drawing on the cover of this book is less then 500kb.

Stardraw 2D

Stardraw 2D is a very much database driven lighting program with CAD capabilities. Much of its functionality is geared towards producing reports for the LX department. As is obvious from the title, this version is two-dimensional only.

Both the Test 2000 drawing imported via File ➤ Open then selecting AutoCAD DWG Files in the drop down. A units selection box opens *Fig 10-18*. Make sure you select 1 unit = millimetres. Blocks were discarded but the Layers remained intact *Fig 10-19*.

As there were no sample files included, I created a simple drawing with a couple of lines, an ellipse and a few lanterns *Fig10-20*. The drawing was saved as a Stardraw file then exported as an AutoCAD 2004 file via File ➤ Save as. Again, the unit selection box was offered so make sure the units are correct. This is a common

10-18 Define DWG/DXF units dialogue box in Stardraw. These boxes are common in most programs for both Importing and exporting files.

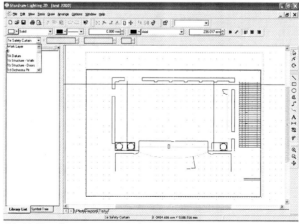

10-19 Test drawing imported into Stardraw as a 2D drawing.

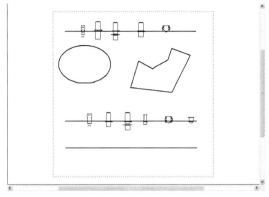

10-20 Sample drawing created by myself in Stardraw, as it appeared in AutoCAD.

feature when exporting files via dwg/dxf so make sure that the units the drawing is created in and those you wish to export it in are the same. Great confusion in scale can occur if this simple rule is not observed. Saving a drawing as millimetres originally drawn in inches is very confusing to anyone trying to take a measurement from the resulting drawing.

The drawing opened in AutoCAD and all the lantern symbols became blocks so can be reused. Unfortunately none of the attribute information was there. Although some numbers are on the drawing, they are just text within the block and can only be amended once the block is exploded. The line thickness also disappeared upon import.

SoftPlot 8

SoftPlot is another lighting program, created by Crescit. It is not widely used in the UK but is quite a nice program with the ability to create 3D drawings and draw-your-own Lantern Symbols.

Prior to importing our drawing, some setting up is required in SoftPlot. Firstly,

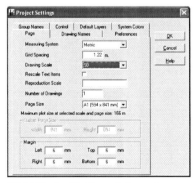

10-21 Project Settings dialogue in SoftPlot. As A0 was not available the sheet size was changed to 1-50 at A1.

we need to set the sheet size to accommodate the drawing. Click Settings ➢ Page to open the dialogue box and set them as shown *Fig 10-21*. As SoftPlot doesn't support printing to A0 size we will have to make do with 1:50 on A1.

Now we have the correct sheet we can import a dxf file by clicking File ➢ Import DXF. Another dialogue box will open: make sure millimetres is selected then click Import DXF then Close when it has finished processing the file *Fig 10-22*. Using Edit ➢ Sheet origin I have centred the drawing up within the sheet outline. The border on our drawing seems to have been altered in the import and is not complete. In some ways, this is a simplified version of the original file. Also, the 3D information in the drawing is not read although SoftPlot does work in 3D.

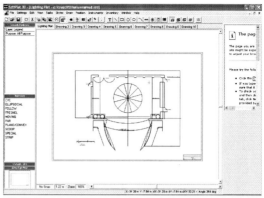

10-22 Test drawing opened in SoftPlot as a dxf. All 3D information has been discarded.

The Layer system in SoftPlot will put everything onto one Layer. This means a lot of Layer editing to rebuild the standard format.

To see how a SoftPlot file exports into AutoCAD, I opened the theatresample file from the Task Manager – Open Existing Lighting Plot tab and exported it to AutoCAD as a .dxf. This is done by clicking File ➢ Export DXF *Fig 10-23.*

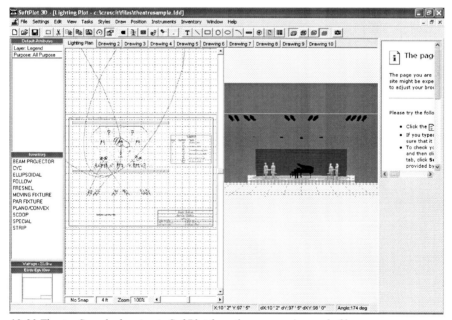

10-23 Theatre Sample drawing in SoftPlot from the program's sample files.

Unfortunately, I consistently got this error message in AutoCAD regardless of version and thus was unable to import the file to check it.

```
Duplicate definition of block PIANO_GRAND on
line 125696.
Invalid or incomplete DXF input — drawing
discarded.
Regenerating model.
```

This also applied to a test .dxf file, which is part of the SoftPlot installation and a dxf file I created from a native SoftPlot file.

WYSIWYG

WYSIWYG is a lighting package in several parts, ranging from simple rig plans to full rendering and cue creation. To view 3D files you must have at least WYSIWYG Design. Importing AutoCAD 3D Solids has always been a problem in WYSIWYG, but one that the current Release 10 has overcome. There is a workaround, for earlier releases, which is as follows.

Open the AutoCAD drawing then click File ➢ Export to open a standard save dialogue box entitled Export Data. Change the file type to 3D Studio (.3ds) it should be noted that this is not a 3DS Max file, which uses the .max file format.

Create a file name and click Save. In AutoCAD the command line reads:

10-24 3D Studio file options dialogue. 3DS is required to export 3D information into WYSIWYG up to Release 9.

```
Command: _export

Select objects: Type all

577 found

Select objects: ↵
```

The 3D Studio File Export Options dialogue box will open but just click OK to accept the defaults *Fig 10-24*. The command line will now go through an automatic sequence to convert the file, this may take a little time, so be patient. The sequence starts with:

```
Command: _3DSOUT

Initializing Render...

Loading materials...done.
```

```
Select objects: _P
577 found
Select objects:
```

The sequence ends with:

```
3D Studio file output
completed
```

Once you see the final message, you can close the drawing. Now open a fresh drawing and import the 3D Studio drawing by clicking Insert ➤ 3D Studio and navigating to where you saved the file.

10-25 Import Options for 3DS in order to create a usable 3D file to send into WYSIWYG.

Once you open the file you will be shown a 3D Studio File Import Options dialogue *Fig10-25*. In the top area click Add All to move all the layers and therefore objects across to the other box. Next, click OK. Another dialogue box may appear to warn you of materials being split across layers. Click OK to proceed and the drawing will open. You may have to use Zoom extents to see it but once you have, change to an Isometric view *Fig 10-26*.

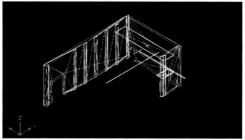

10-26 3DS file in AutoCAD. The 3D Solids have been broken up into polygonal surfaces.

As you can see, we now have solids made with Polygons, all layer colour has gone and the number of layers reduced, but we can now import this drawing into WYSIWYG. Save it as an AutoCAD 2000 drawing and close AutoCAD.

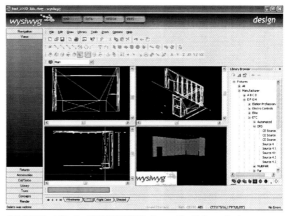

10-27 Test file in WYSIWYG Release 7. Although the polygons are obvious in the wireframe views they do not show in the Shaded viewport.

Our dwg can now be opened in WYSIWYG by choosing Open Existing Plot – More… and navigating to the drawing from the Welcome screen. You will need to change the file type from .wyg to .dwg then select millimetres and make sure that the Layers you want are imported from the dialogue box that will appear. You will get a new dialogue box asking what you want to do with any blocks in the drawing. Generally speaking you can use the Skip button to pass through this process, after which the drawing will open *Fig 10-27*. As you can see the polygon construction remains but when it is put into WYSIWYG's shaded view the walls work just as they would if constructed in WYSIWYG.

WYSIWYG Release 10

The newest version of WYSIWYG (at the time of writing) is Release 10 and the problems with importing AutoCAD 3D Solids have now been solved as shown by *Figs 10 –28, 10-29*. This makes things a lot easier all round and is a very persuasive argument for upgrading if you do deal with a lot of 3D modelling originating in AutoCAD.

I used the Theatre – dance plot.wyg sample drawing to test export to AutoCAD. You can export from any tab except shaded *Fig 10-30*.

Click File ➤ Dwg/DXF Export. If you only have the Report level of WYSIWYG then 2D DWG/DXF Export is your only option. You can however

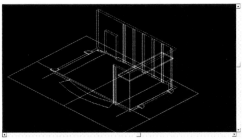

10-28 Test drawing when directly imported into WYSIWYG 10.

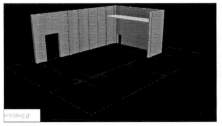

10-29 Shaded View of the Test drawing in WYSIWYG 10. Direct importation of the 3D Solids keeps the Layers also.

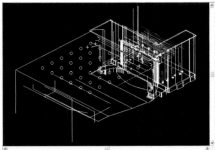

10-30 Theatre – Dance plot sample .wyg

export any of the available views. An Export dialogue box will open giving the choice of .dwg formats to save to. When you have selcted the file type, clicking Save will open the DWG Settings dialogue box. Check you are using the correct units and which layers are to be exported and click OK.

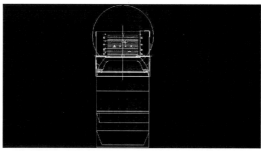

10-31 Theatre – Dance plot as a .dwg in AutoCAD. Note how the arc front of the stage has turned into a mirror of itself.

When opened in AutoCAD the drawing is in Plan view *Fig 10-31*. The only difference between the drawings is that the curved stage front seems to have become a mirror image of itself, hence the large incomplete circle upstage.

If you zoom in to the drawing, you will see that the lanterns have imported as fully three dimensional objects. Although none of the data associated with the lamps has been imported, it is nonetheless useful having a fully 3D representation of how much space will be taken up by LX, especially on those shows with a tight grid *Fig 10-32*.

10-32 Shaded close up view in AutoCAD of the LX rig. Having the lamps as full 3 Dimensional objects is very useful in understanding the spatial relationships in the grid.

SketchUp 4

SketchUp, by @Last Software is primarily an architectural application that is also gradually being used in the entertainment industry for creating 3D models quickly and without a great deal of program knowledge. The latest version is 4, and there is now a plug in available for Film, providing a 16:9 mask and other film set objects such as camera cranes and dollies.

The test 2000.dwg was inserted via File ➤ Insert ➤ DWG/DXF. As you can see the 3D Solids appear as they do in the 3DS version for WYSIWYG. The Layers are however all imported complete, although the Layer colours must be turned on *Fig 10-33*.

I next opened a SketchUp drawing from the Film and Stage plug in – a 125W HMI Lantern. As you can see this is the most 'graphic' looking file *Fig 10-34*. I exported it to AutoCAD using File ➤ Export ➤ 3D Model and saved it as the default: AutoCAD.dwg.

The file imported into AutoCAD with no problems but has lost the textured shadows that makes it look so different in SketchUp *Fig 10-35*. When

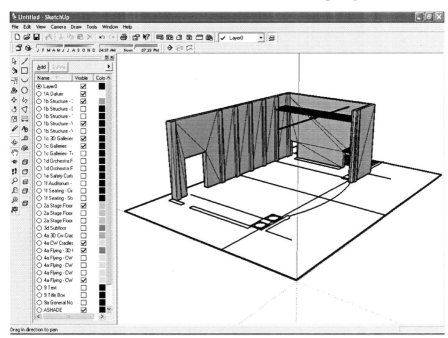

10-33 Test drawing in SketchUp. Again, the 3D Solids have been broken up into polygonal surfaces.

converted to a .dwg the SketchUp model has turned into a series of surfaces which although they look like 3D solids are not. This does not really affect the use of them in AutoCAD however.

Unfortunately, as is common with all these programs, materials do not translate across but a lot of work is still saved by exchanging drawings between the various programs used in the industry.

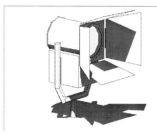

10-34 SketchUp 125w HMI Lantern included in the Film & Set Plug In. Note the interesting shadow automatically created within SketchUp.

All of these programs are used within the industry and as can be seen from my experiences it is important to establish what 'flavour' of .dwg everyone should work to so that drawings can be confidently exchanged.

The change of dwg file format from AutoCAD 2000 to 2004 has proved particularly problematic for many rival software vendors as both compression (leading to a much smaller file size) and encryption, were used for the first time. As a result, the delay in other programs being able to offer dwg to this format has been longer than is normal despite the best

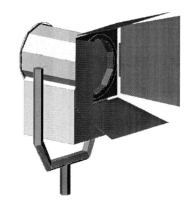

10-35 The HMI Lantern imported into AutoCAD.

efforts of the Open Design Alliance. It is partly for this reason that I recommend saving your AutoCAD files as 2000.dwg until everyone has caught up.

Scale Conversions

Tip!

The first thing to remember is that this Scale is the one that uses the crossing window or polygon. Therefore, to change a scale you must firstly import the drawing then Scale the whole thing. Use 0,0, as the base point to scale from so that the UCS/WCS remains constant. Obviously, you will need to know what units the drawing was created in to scale correctly.

You may have to make the odd educated guess, for instance 30 feet, a common prosc size, is 360 inches. If you import a drawing from Imperial units into a metric drawing you will end up with a prosc of either 30mm or 360mm wide, which although it will probably help the masking is a bit narrow. In either case, the metric distance is 9145mm.

If you make a habit of importing drawings whose scale you are unsure of into a standard template, complete with scale bar, then you should be able to judge the originating units and scale accordingly. Obviously if the incoming drawing has a scale bar or a dimension this makes life easier.

What is ideal is if everyone draws to the same units from the off, but this is not always possible, particularly with shows that are revivals or foreign productions. There is also the problem of those who draw using CAD to no particular size but so that, to their eyes, 'it looks right'. These are often the most difficult drawings to deal with and often the only way to resolve them is to contact whoever created them and get at least one reference dimension — even if it is approximate — and scale from that object.

With such situations, accuracy cannot be guaranteed and large health warnings are recommended on the drawings, so that everyone is clear as to the tenuousness of the measurements.

As most CAD drawings are in either in Millimetres (Metric) or Feet and/or Inches (Imperial, English or Architectural) I have only included a small table.

Feet	to	Millimetres	Scale by	305
Inches	to	Millimetres	Scale by	25.4
Millimetres	to	Feet	Scale by	0.00328
Millimetres	to	Inches	Scale by	0.03937

Comparative File sizes all based on the Test drawing used above

Program	File extension	File size
AutoCAD 2000	.dwg	192kb
AutoCAD 2004	.dwg	102kb
Drawing Exchange File	.dxf	1424kb
TurboCAD 10	.tcw	91kb
SketchUp	.skp	170kb
SoftPlot 8*	.lld	3120kb
Stardraw 2D*	.s01	95kb
VectorWorks Spotlight	.mcd	696kb
WYSIWYG	.wyg	1939kb
3D Studio	.3DS	403kb

* 2D File only created

BIBLIOGRAPHY

AutoCAD Users Guide
You will have to return the card included in the software packaging to get it but it is a very useful reference.
Autodesk Part no 00125-010000-5020A

AutoCAD Help Files
Press F1 for AutoCAD help divided into Reference, Concept and Procedures for each command.

AutoCAD 2004 Bible *Ellen Finkelstein. Wiley Publishing. ISBN: 0 7645 3992 2. £34.95*
A weighty tome, but I find it an invaluable reference to have to hand.

Computer Visualisation for the Theatre *Gavin Carver and Christine White. Focal Press. ISBN: 0240516176. £19.99*
Covers the use of 3D Modelling (mainly 3D Viz) in a theatrical context.

Scenery Construction and Draughting *John Blurton. A&C Black. ISBN: 0713656840. £14.99*
Covers draughting techniques, in a theatrical context.

Web Resources
CAD Programs

AutoCAD	www.autocad.com
TurboCAD	www.imsi.com
VectorWorks	www.nemetschek.net
Stardraw	www.stardraw.com
SoftPlot	www.crescit.com
WYSIWYG	www.castlighting.com
SketchUp	www.sketchup.com
3DS Max & Viz	www.discreet.com
LD Assistant	www.ldassistant.com

Organisations and Standards

Open Design Alliance	www.opendesign.com
ABTT CAD Standards	www.cad4theatre.org.uk
USITT CAD Standards	www.usitt.org

Theatre Resources

Modelbox	www.modelbox.co.uk
Digital Set Design (Roma Patel)	www.digitalsetdesign.com
KiDDS (Kent Interactive Digital Design Studio)	www.kent.ac.uk/sdfva/kidds/

General CAD Resources

AutoCAD Shareware Clearing House	www.cadalog.com
The CAD Depot	www.caddedpot.com
Cadalyst Magazine	www.cadalyst.com

INDEX

ENTERTAINMENT TECHNOLOGY PRESS

FREE SUBSCRIPTION SERVICE

Keeping Up To Date with

Autocad - A Handbook for Theatre Users

Entertainment Technology titles are continually up-dated, and all major changes and additions are listed in date order in the relevant dedicated area of the publisher's website. Simply go to the front page of www.etnow.com and click on the BOOKS button. From there you can locate the title and be connected through to the latest information and services related to the publication.

The author of the title welcomes comments and suggestions about the book and can be contacted by email at: david@cad4theatre.org.uk

Titles Published by Entertainment Technology Press

ABC of Theatre Jargon *Francis Reid* **£9.95** ISBN 1904031099
This glossary of theatrical terminology explains the common words and phrases that are
used in normal conversation between actors, directors, designers, technicians and managers.

Aluminium Structures in the Entertainment Industry *Peter Hind* **£24.95**
ISBN 1904031064
Aluminium Structures in the Entertainment Industry aims to educate the reader in all aspects
of the design and safe usage of temporary and permanent aluminium structures specific to
the entertainment industry – such as roof structures, PA towers, temporary staging, etc.

AutoCAD – A Handbook for Theatre Users *David Ripley* **£24.95** ISBN 1904031315
From 'Setting Up' to 'Drawing in Three Dimensions' via 'Drawings Within Drawings', this
compact and fully illustrated guide to AutoCAD covers everything from the basics to full
colour rendering and remote plotting.

Basics - A Beginner's Guide to Stage Lighting *Peter Coleman* **£9.95** ISBN 190403120X
This title does what it says: it introduces newcomers to the world of stage lighting. It will
not teach the reader the art of lighting design, but will teach beginners much about the 'nuts
and bolts' of stage lighting.

Basics - A Beginner's Guide to Stage Sound *Peter Coleman* **£9.95** ISBN 1904031277
This title does what it says: it introduces newcomers to the world of stage sound. It will not
teach the reader the art of sound design, but will teach beginners much about the 'nuts and
bolts' of stage lighting.

A Comparative Study of Crowd Behaviour at Two Major Music Events
ISBN 1904031250
Chris Kemp, Iain Hill, Mick Upton **£7.95** ISBN 1904031099
A compilation of the findings of reports made at two major live music concerts, and in
particular crowd behaviour, which is followed from ingress to egress.

Electrical Safety for Live Events *Marco van Beek* **£16.95** ISBN 1904031285
This title covers electrical safety regulations and good pracitise pertinent to the
entertainment industries and includes some basic electrical theory as well as clarifying the
"do's and don't's" of working with electricity.

The Exeter Theatre Fire *David Anderson* **£24.95** ISBN 1904031137
This title is a fascinating insight into the events that led up to the disaster at the Theatre
Royal, Exeter, on the night of September 5th 1887. The book details what went wrong, and
the lessons that were learned from the event.

Focus on Lighting Technology *Richard Cadena* **£17.95** ISBN 1904031145
This concise work unravels the mechanics behind modern performance lighting and appeals
to designers and technicians alike. Packed with clear, easy-to-read diagrams, the book
provides excellent explanations behind the technology of performance lighting.

Health and Safety Aspects in the Live Music Industry *Chris Kemp, Iain Hill* **£30.00**
ISBN 1904031226
This title includes chapters on various safety aspects of live event production and is written
by specialists in their particular areas of expertise.

Health and Safety Management in the Live Music and Events Industry *Chris Hannam*
£25.95 ISBN 1904031307
This title covers the health and safety regulations and their application regarding all aspects of staging live entertainment events, and is an invaluable manual for production managers and event organisers.

Hearing the Light *Francis Reid* **£24.95** ISBN 1904031188
This highly enjoyable memoir delves deeply into the theatricality of the industry. The author's almost fanatical interest in opera, his formative period as lighting designer at Glyndebourne and his experiences as a theatre administrator, writer and teacher make for a broad and unique background.

An Introduction to Rigging in the Entertainment Industry *Chris Higgs* **£24.95**
ISBN 1904031129
This book is a practical guide to rigging techniques and practices and also thoroughly covers safety issues and discusses the implications of working within recommended guidelines and regulations.

Let There be Light - Entertainment Lighting Software Pioneers in Interview
Robert Bell **£32.00** ISBN 1904031242
Robert Bell interviews an assortment of software engineers working on entertainment lighting products.

Lighting for Roméo and Juliette *John Offord* **£26.95** ISBN 1904031161
John Offord describes the making of the production from the lighting designer's viewpoint - taking the story through from the point where director Jürgen Flimm made his decision not to use scenery or sets and simply employ the expertise of Patrick Woodroffe.

Lighting Systems for TV Studios *Nick Mobsby* **£35.00** ISBN 1904031005
Lighting Systems for TV Studios is the first book written specifically on the subject and is set to become the 'standard' resource work for the sector as it covers all elements of system design – rigging, ventilation, electrical as well as the more obvious controls, dimmers and luminaires.

Lighting Techniques for Theatre-in-the-Round *Jackie Staines* **£24.95** ISBN 1904031013
Lighting Techniques for Theatre-in-the-Round is a unique reference source for those working on lighting design for theatre-in-the-round for the first time. It is the first title to be published specifically on the subject, it also provides some anecdotes and ideas for more challenging shows, and attempts to blow away some of the myths surrounding lighting in this format.

Lighting the Stage *Francis Reid* **£14.95** ISBN 1904031080
Lighting the Stage discusses the human relationships involved in lighting design – both between people, and between these people and technology. The book is written from a highly personal viewpoint and its 'thinking aloud' approach is one that Francis Reid has used in his writings over the past 30 years.

Model National Standard Conditions *ABTT/DSA/LGLA* **£20.00** ISBN 1904031110
These *Model National Standard Conditions* covers operational matters and complement *The Technical Standards for Places of Entertainment*, which describes the physical requirements for building and maintaining entertainment premises.

Pages From Stages *Anthony Field* **£17.95** ISBN 1904031269
Anthony Field explores the changing style of theatres including interior design, exterior design, ticket and seat prices, and levels of service, while questioning whether the theatre still exists as a place of entertainment for regular theatre-goers.

Practical Guide to Health and Safety in the Entertainment Industry
Marco van Beek **£14.95** ISBN 1904031048
This book is designed to provide a practical approach to Health and Safety within the Live Entertainment and Event industry. It gives industry-pertinent examples, and seeks to break down the myths surrounding Health and Safety.

Production Management *Joe Aveline* **£17.95** ISBN 1904031102
Joe Aveline's book is an in-depth guide to the role of the Production Manager, and includes real-life practical examples and 'Aveline's Fables' – anecdotes of his experiences with real messages behind them.

Rigging for Entertainment: Regulations and Practice *Chris Higgs* **£19.95**
ISBN 1904031218
Continuing where he left off with his highly successful *An Introduction to Rigging in the Entertainment Industry*, Chris Higgs' new book covers the regulations and use of equipment in greater detail.

Rock Solid Ethernet *Wayne Howell* **£24.95** ISBN 1904031293
Although aimed specifically at specifiers, installers and users of entertainment industry systems, this book will give the reader a thorough grounding in all aspects of computer networks, whatever industry they may work in. The inclusion of historical and technical 'sidebars' in this book makes for an enjoyable as well as informative read.

Sixty Years of Light Work *Fred Bentham* **£26.95** ISBN 1904031072
This title is an autobiography of one of the great names behind the development of modern stage lighting equipment and techniques.

Sound for the Stage *Patrick Finelli* **£24.95** ISBN 1904031153
Patrick Finelli's thorough manual covering all aspects of live and recorded sound for performance is a complete training course for anyone interested in working in the field of stage sound, and is a must for any student of sound.

Stage Lighting for Theatre Designers *Nigel Morgan* **£17.95** ISBN 1904031196
An updated second edition of this popular book for students of theatre design outlining all the techniques of stage lighting design.

Technical Marketing Techniques *David Brooks, Andy Collier, Steve Norman* **£24.95**
ISBN 190403103X
Technical Marketing is a novel concept, recently defined and elaborated by the authors of this book, with business-to-business companies competing in fast developing technical product sectors.

Technical Standards for Places of Entertainment *ABTT/DSA* **£30.00** ISBN 1904031056
Technical Standards for Places of Entertainment details the necessary physical standards required for entertainment venues.

Theatre Engineering and Stage Machinery *Toshiro Ogawa* **£30.00** ISBN 1904031021
Theatre Engineering and Stage Machinery is a unique reference work covering every aspect of theatrical machinery and stage technology in global terms.

Theatre Lighting in the Age of Gas *Terence Rees* **£24.95** ISBN 190403117X
Entertainment Technology Press is delighted to be republishing this valuable historic work
previously produced by the Society for Theatre Research in 1978. *Theatre Lighting in the
Age of Gas* investigates the technological and artistic achievements of theatre lighting
engineers from the 1700s to the late Victorian period.

Walt Disney Concert Hall *Patricia MacKay & Richard Pilbrow* **£28.95** ISBN 1904031234
Spanning the 16-year history of the design and construction of the Walt Disney Concert
Hall, this book provides a fresh and detailed, behind the scenes story of the design and
technology from a variety of viewpoints. This is the first book to reveal the "process" of the
design of a concert hall.

Yesterday's Lights – A Revolution Reported *Francis Reid* **£26.95** ISBN 1904031323
Set to help new generations to be aware of where the art and science of theatre lighting is
coming from – and stimulate a nostalgia trip for those who lived through the period, Francis
Reid's latest book has over 350 pages dedicated to the task, covering the 'revolution' from
the fifties through to the present day. Although this is a highly personal account of the
development of lighting design and technology and he admits that there are 'gaps', you'd be
hard put to find anything of significance missing.

Go to www.etbooks.co.uk for full details of above titles and secure online ordering facilities.